"By the Talking River
You and I
And a Dragon Fly,
Gauzy wings a quiver."

*(From a drawing by Graham Robertson in " Baby's Day Book,"
by kind permission.)*

The " Teaching of English" Series

General Editor—SIR HENRY NEWBOLT

PATTERN POETRY

PART I-A

No. 121

PATTERN POETRY

Part I-A

A Book of Poems of Incident
and Narration

Arranged by
RICHARD WILSON

THOMAS NELSON & SONS, Ltd.
LONDON, EDINBURGH. AND NEW YORK

First published July 1927.
Reprinted January 1928; March 1929.

PREFACE

THE exercises and commentary following each poem are addressed to the pupil, and are intended to be used for individual work to be done before the poem is taken by the class.

This book will provide an alternative introduction to *Pattern Poetry*, Part I., for those teachers who prefer to begin with narrative poetry only. Or it can be used to follow Part I., being, on the whole, a little more difficult, though not much.

For permission to use copyright pieces thanks are due and are hereby tendered to :

Messrs. Longmans, Green, and Co., Ltd., for " Echo and the Ferry" and "Martin's Gift" by Jean Ingelow; Mr. Alfred Noyes and Messrs. Blackwood and Sons, Ltd., for " The Highwayman"; Mr. Padraic Colum for "The Ballad-Maker"; Messrs. John Lane, the Bodley Head, Ltd., and Miss Rosamund Marriott Watson, for " A Ballad of Pentyre Town"; Mrs. Katharine Tynan Hinkson for " Of St. Francis and the Ass"; Mr. Walter de la Mare for "Sam's Three Wishes"; the Rev. R. L. Gales and Messrs. Simpkin, Marshall, Ltd., for " A Ballad of St. Christopher "; and Mr. Anstey Guthrie for " The Wreck of the Steamship ' Puffin.' "

R. W.

CONTENTS

PATTERN POETRY

PART I-A

Johnny Head-in-Air

As he slowly trudged to school,
It was heedless Johnny's rule
To keep looking at the sky
And the clouds that floated by :
But what just before him lay
In his way,
Johnny never thought about :
So that every one cried out,
" Look at little Johnny there,
Little Johnny Head-in-Air ! "

Running just in Johnny's way,
Came a little dog one day ;
Johnny's eyes were still astray
Up on high,
In the sky ;
And he never heard them cry—
" Johnny, mind, the dog is nigh ! "
Bump !
Dump !
Down they fell with such a thump !
Dog and Johnny in a lump !

Once with head as high as ever
Johnny walked beside the river,
Johnny watched the swallows trying
Which was cleverest at flying.
Oh ! what fun !
Johnny watched the bright-red sun
Going in and coming out ;
This was all he thought about.
So he strode on, only think !
To the river's very brink,
Where the bank was high and steep,
And the water very deep ;
And the fishes in a row,
Stared to see him coming so.

One step more ! Oh ! sad to tell !
Headlong in poor Johnny fell.
And the fishes in dismay
Wagged their tails and ran away.
There lay Johnny on his face,
With his nice red writing-case ;
But, as they were passing by,
Two strong men had heard him cry ;
And with sticks these two strong men
Hooked poor Johnny out again.

Oh ! you should have seen him shiver
When they pulled him from the river.
He was in a sorry plight,
Dripping wet and such a fright !
Wet all over, everywhere,
Clothes, and arms, and face, and hair :
Johnny never will forget
What it is to be *so* wet.

And the fishes, one, two, three,
All came back again, you see ;
Up they came the moment after,
To enjoy the fun and laughter.

Each popped out his little head,
And, to tease poor Johnny, said,
" Silly little Johnny, look,
You have lost your writing-book ! "

From *Shock-headed Peter*.

These verses show how they taught " Safety First " a hundred or more years ago. Johnny would be dressed like the boy in the picture. How he would have laughed at the way *you* dress !

And what would have happened to him in one of our big towns or in London ! Perhaps you can write a few lines about his adventures in London of to-day. You might begin :

" Down the crowded London street—"

The verses make you think of pictures, one after the other, like a film. Try to draw one in which the fishes appear.

What have you noticed about (1) the verses or stanzas ; (2) the lines in this poem ?

The Story of Augustus who would not have any Soup

AUGUSTUS was a chubby lad ;
Fat, ruddy cheeks Augustus had ;
And everybody saw with joy
The plump and hearty, healthy boy.
He ate and drank as he was told,
And never let his soup get cold.
But one day, one cold winter's day,
He screamed out—" Take the soup away :
Oh, take the nasty soup away !
I won't have any soup to-day."

Next day begins his tale of woes,
Quite lank and lean Augustus grows.

Yet though he feels so weak and ill,
The naughty fellow cries out still—
" Not any soup for me, I say :
Oh, take the nasty soup away !
I won't have any soup to-day."

The third day comes ; oh, what a sin !
To make himself so pale and thin.
Yet, when the soup is put on table,
He screams, as loud as he is able,—
" Not any soup for me, I say :
Oh, take the nasty soup away !
I won't have any soup to-day."

Look at him, now the fourth day's come !
He scarcely weighs a sugar-plum ;
He's like a little bit of thread,
And on the fifth day, he was—dead !

From *Shock-headed Peter.*

These verses also belong to the time of Johnny Head-in-Air. What do you think about Augustus and about the food in his home ?

What foods do we never seem to tire of ? Try to alter the verses to make them suit one of these foods, and so end quite suitably with the end of Augustus.

You might call the boy in your verses Marmaduke. If you do, you will have to alter the second line a good deal.

Are all the stanzas of the same length ? Does it seem to matter ?

The Dreadful Story about Harriet and the Matches

IT almost makes me cry to tell
What foolish Harriet befell.
Mamma and Nurse went out one day
And left her all alone at play ;

Now, on the table close at hand,
A box of matches chanced to stand ;
And kind Mamma and Nurse had told her
That, if she touched them, they should scold her.
But Harriet said : " Oh, what a pity !
For, when they burn, it is so pretty ;
They crackle so, and spit, and flame ;
Mamma, too, often does the same."

The pussy-cats heard this,
And they began to hiss,
And stretch their claws
And raise their paws ;
" Me-ow," they said, " me-ow, me-o,
You'll burn to death, if you do so."

But Harriet would not take advice,
She lit a match, it was so nice !
It crackled so, it burned so bright,
It filled her with immense delight.
She jumped for joy and ran about
And was too pleased to put it out.

The pussy-cats saw this
And said : " Oh, naughty, naughty Miss ! "
And stretched their claws
And raised their paws :
" 'Tis very, very wrong, you know,
Me-ow, me-o, me-ow, me-o,
You will be burnt, if you do so."

And see ! oh what a dreadful thing !
The fire has caught her apron-string ;
Her apron burns, her arms, her hair ;
She burns all over, everywhere.

Then how the pussy-cats did mew,
What else, poor pussies, could they do ?

They screamed for help, 'twas all in vain !
So then they said : " We'll scream again ;
Make haste, make haste, me-ow, me-o,
She'll burn to death, we told her so."

So she was burnt, with all her clothes,
And arms, and hands, and eyes, and
    nose :
Till she had nothing more to lose
Except her little scarlet shoes ;
And nothing else but these were found
Among her ashes on the ground.

And when the good cats sat beside
The smoking ashes, how they cried !
" Me-ow, me-oo, me-ow, me-oo,
What will Mamma and Nursy do ? "
Their tears ran down their cheeks so fast,
They made a little pond at last.

From *Shock-headed Peter.*

Harriet might be the little girl in the picture on page
10, while Mamma (and Papa) would look like the people
in the picture on this page.

This is another set of " Safety First " verses. It is
interesting to remember that our safety matches had
not been invented in Harriet's time ; but even safety
matches are not good playthings, as you do not need to
be told. How does the writer take away some of the
dreadfulness of the story ?

Could you write a few lines making out that Harriet
was badly burnt but that her life was saved—say, by the
cats ? (This will not be easy, but it is good fun to try.)

The Mouse and the Cake

A MOUSE found a beautiful piece of plum-cake,
The richest and sweetest that mortal could make ;

'Twas heavy with citron and fragrant with spice,
And covered with sugar all sparkling as ice.

" My stars ! " cried the mouse, while his eye beamed
    with glee,
" Here's a treasure I've found ; what a feast it will
    be :
But, hark ! there's a noise, 'tis my brothers at play ;
So I'll hide with the cake, lest they wander this way.

" Not a bit shall they have, for I know I can eat
Every morsel myself, and I'll have such a treat ; "
So off went the mouse, as he held the cake fast,
While his hungry young brothers went scampering
    past.

He nibbled, and nibbled, and panted, but still
He kept gulping it down till he made himself ill ;
Yet he swallowed it all, and 'tis easy to guess,
He was soon so unwell that he groaned with distress.

His family heard him, and as he grew worse,
They sent for the doctor, who made him rehearse
How he'd eaten the cake to the very last crumb,
Without giving his playmates and relatives some.

" Ah me ! " cried the doctor, " advice is too late,
You must die before long, so prepare for your fate ;
If you had but divided the cake with your brothers,
'Twould have done you no harm, and been good for
    the others.

" Had you shared it, the treat had been wholesome
    enough ;
But eaten by one, it was dangerous stuff ;
So prepare for the worst ; " and the word had scarce
    fled,
When the doctor turned round, and the patient was
    dead.

Now all little people the lesson may take,
And some large ones may learn from the mouse and
the cake,
Not to be over-selfish with what we may gain ;
Or the best of our pleasures may turn into pain.

ELIZA COOK.

This is an improving story of the time of Johnny
Head-in-Air, quite sensible and good for any period.

And quite well told too. It goes with a swing, and has
a certain amount of quiet fun, with good word-pictures.
Which would make the funniest drawing ?

It was clever of the writer to make the story about a
mouse instead of about a greedy boy. The idea, however,
is old. Many hundreds of years ago a Greek writer named
Æsop used the animal story to teach a lesson. Here is
one of his Fables, which you might try to put into verses :

THE DOG, THE COCK, AND THE FOX

A dog and a cock having made friends went out on their
travels together. Night found them in a wood. So the
cock, flying up into a tree, perched among the branches,
while the dog slept below at the foot. The night passed
away and the day dawned. Then the cock, as he always
does, set up a shrill crowing. A fox hearing him, and
thinking to make a meal of him, came and stood under
the tree. He said to the cock :

" Thou art a good little bird, and hast a fine voice.
Come down, then, that we may sing our morning hymn
and be glad together."

In reply the cock said : " Go, my good friend, to the
foot of the tree, and call the priest to toll the bell."

But, as the fox went to call him, he was met by the
big dog, who jumped upon him, and killed him in a very
few minutes.

Moral.—It is a good thing to see the plans of the wicked
defeated by the wisdom of the innocent. The wiles of
the crafty are often ruinous to themselves.

Meddlesome Matty

ONE ugly trick has often spoiled
  The sweetest and the best ;
Matilda, though a pleasant child,
  One ugly trick possessed,
Which, like a cloud before the skies,
Hid all her better qualities.

Sometimes she'd lift the tea-pot lid,
  To peep at what was in it ;
Or tilt the kettle, if you did
  But turn your back a minute ;
In vain you told her not to touch,
Her trick of meddling grew so much.

Her grandmamma went out one day,
  And by mistake she laid
Her spectacles and snuff-box gay
  Too near the little maid ;
" Ah ! well," thought she, " I'll try them on,
As soon as grandmamma is gone."

Forthwith she placed upon her nose
  The glasses large and wide ;
And looking round, as I suppose,
  The snuff-box, too, she spied :
" Oh ! what a pretty box is that ;
I'll open it," said little Mat.

" I know that grandmamma would say,
  ' Don't meddle with it, dear ' ;
But then, she's far enough away,
  And no one else is near :
Besides, what can there be amiss
In opening such a box as this ? "
(2,873)

2

So thumb and finger went to work
  To move the stubborn lid,
And presently a mighty jerk
  The mighty mischief did ;
For all at once, ah ! woeful case,
The snuff came puffing in her face.

Poor eyes and nose, and mouth beside,
  A dismal sight presented ;
In vain, as bitterly she cried,
  Her folly she repented.
In vain she ran about for ease ;
She could do nothing now but sneeze.

She dashed the spectacles away,
  To wipe her tingling eyes,
And as in twenty bits they lay,
  Her grandmamma she spies.
" Hey-day ! and what's the matter now ? "
Says grandmamma, with lifted brow.

Matilda, smarting with the pain,
  And tingling still, and sore,
Made many a promise to refrain
  From meddling evermore.
And 'tis a fact, as I have heard,
She ever since has kept her word.

ANN TAYLOR.

Æsop would have told this story about a cat or a rat
in a larder in which there was a cruet-stand or box of
pepper. I wonder, however, whether there were any
cruet-stands or pepper in ancient Greece ? But that is
a small matter. Perhaps you could make it up, and
even put some of it into verses.

Which part of the story tells you at once that it
belongs to an earlier time than our own ?

Is snuff ever used now, and if so, for what purpose ?

The Bad Boy

ONCE a little round-eyed lad
Determined to be very bad.

He called his porridge nasty pap,
And threw it all in nurse's lap.

His gentle sister's cheek he hurt,
He smudged his pinny in the dirt.

He found the bellows, and he blew
The pet canary right in two !

And when he went to bed at night
He would not say his prayers aright.

This pained a lovely twinkling star
That watched the trouble from afar.

She told her bright-faced friends, and soon
The dreadful rumour reached the moon.

The moon, a gossiping old dame,
Told Father Sun the bad boy's shame.

And then the giant sun began
A very satisfactory plan.

Upon the naughty rebel's face
He would not pour his beamy grace.

He would not stroke the dark-brown strands
With entertaining shiny hands.

The little garden of the boy
Seemed desert, missing heaven's joy.

But all his sister's tulips grew
Magnificent with shine and dew.

Where'er he went he found a shade,
But light was poured upon the maid.

He also lost, by his disgrace,
That indoors sun, his mother's face.

His father sent him up to bed
With neither kiss nor pat for head.

And in his sleep he had such foes,
Bad fairies pinched his curling toes—

They bit his ears, they pulled his hairs,
They threw him three times down the stairs.

Oh, little boys who would not miss
A father's and a mother's kiss,

Who would not cause a sister pain,
Who want the sun to shine again,

Who want sweet beams to tend the plot
Where grows the pet forget-me-not,

Who hate a life of streaming eyes,
Be good, be merry, and be wise.

NORMAN GALE.
(*With acknowledgments.*)

This is a poem somewhat like those you have been
reading, but it belongs to the present day. What is your
thought about it ?

At which parts of the story do you wish to laugh?

Which do you think was the worst thing that happened to the bad boy?

Now try to write a few lines like these about a good boy, but not about a prig. Suppose some one began like this:

> There was a merry strapping youth,
> Who always did what he was told.

What is wrong with the sound?

Do the two lines " step along " properly? (You will have noticed, of course, that verses which please your ear have the sound of *feet* in them.)

The Grey Squirrels

WHEN in my youth I travellèd
  Throughout each north countree,
Many a strange thing did I hear,
  And many a strange thing see.

.   .   .   .   .   .

But nothing was there that pleased me more
  Than when, in autumn brown,
I came, in the depths of the pathless woods,
  To the Grey Squirrels' town.

There were hundreds that in the hollow boles
  Of the old, old trees did dwell,
And laid up store, hard by their door,
  Of the sweet mast as it fell.

But soon the hungry wild swine came,
  And with thievish snouts dug up
Their buried treasure, and left them not
  So much as an acorn cup!

Then did they chatter in angry mood,
   And one and all decree,
Into the forests of rich stone-pine
   Over hill and dale to flee.

Over hill and dale, over hill and dale,
   For many a league they went,
Like a troop of undaunted travellers
   Governed by one consent.

But the hawk and eagle, and peering owl,
   Did dreadfully pursue ;
And the farther the Grey Squirrels went,
   The more their perils grew ;
When lo ! to cut off their pilgrimage,
   A broad stream lay in view.

But then did each wondrous creature show
   His cunning and bravery ;
With a piece of the pine-bark in his mouth,
   Unto the stream came he,

And boldly his little bark he launched,
   Without the least delay ;
His bushy tail was his upright sail,
   And he merrily steered away.

Never was there a lovelier sight
   Than that Grey Squirrels' fleet ;
And with anxious eyes I watched to see
   What fortune it would meet.

Soon had they reached the rough mid-stream,
   And ever and anon
I grieved to behold some small bark wrecked,
   And its little steersman gone.

But the main fleet stoutly held across ;
  I saw them leap to shore ;
They entered the woods with a cry of joy,
  For their perilous march was o'er.

WILLIAM HOWITT.

This is a pretty animal story told about the time of our friend Johnny, and full of charming pictures.

Now the story might have been told in prose. If it had, the first four lines would probably have run :

> When I travelled in my youth through the northern counties I heard and saw many a strange thing.

So to make poetry a writer must (1) make his lines step along in order with regular tread or beat ; (2) measure his lines ; (3) sometimes turn a sentence round ; (4) make rhymes (lines 2 and 4).

Study other four-line verses or stanzas and see whether a poet does other things that a prose writer would not do. In one or two places you will find that he uses special poets' words and phrases, such as " decree " and " to flee."

With these things in mind, look back at poems you have already read. Have all stanzas the same number of lines ?

Earl Haldan's Daughter

It was Earl Haldan's daughter,
  She looked across the sea ;
She looked across the water,
  And long and loud laughed she :
" The locks of six princesses
  Must be my marriage fee,
So hey bonny boat, and ho bonny boat !
  Who comes a-wooing me ? "

It was Earl Haldan's daughter,
  She walked along the strand ;
When she was aware of a knight so fair,
  Come sailing to the land.

His sails were all of velvet,
 His masts of beaten gold,
And hey bonny boat, and ho bonny boat!
 Who saileth here so bold?

" The locks of five princesses
 I won beyond the sea;
I clipt their golden tresses,
 To fringe a cloak for thee.
One handful yet is wanting,
 But one of all the tale;
So hey bonny boat, and ho bonny boat!
 Furl up thy velvet sail!"

He leapt into the water,
 That rover young and bold;
He gript Earl Haldan's daughter,
 He clipt her locks of gold;
" Go weep, go weep, proud maiden,
 The tale is full to-day.
Now hey bonny boat, and ho bonny boat!
 Sail westward ho away!"

CHARLES KINGSLEY.

If you were telling this story in prose, would you say
that the lady looked across the sea and across the water?
And would you say, " The tale is full "—*i.e.*, the full
number is made up?

What is your verdict on this poem, or rather on the
proud princess?

Does the poem tell a story or describe an incident?

Notice how regular the stanzas are, all made to one
pattern, how the words march or even dance along so as
to give the feeling of the moving of the boat. There are
pretty pictures in the poem, one of them full of colour.

Can you find what is called a refrain in these verses?
They were written to be sung, and Rose Salterne sings
them in the author's story, *Westward Ho!*

Choose a short nursery or fairy tale, and try to tell it
like the story of " Earl Haldan's Daughter."

The Wind in a Frolic

THE Wind one morning sprang up from sleep,
Saying, " Now for a frolic ! now for a leap !
Now for a madcap galloping chase !
I'll make a commotion in every place !

So it swept with a bustle right through a great town,
Cracking the signs and scattering down
Shutters ; and whisking, with merciless squalls,
Old women's bonnets and gingerbread stalls.

There never was heard a much lustier shout,
As the apples and oranges trundled about ;
And the urchins that stand with their thievish eyes
For ever on watch, ran off each with a prize.

Then away to the fields it went, blustering and hum-
      ming,
And the cattle all wondered what monster was coming.
It plucked by the tails the grave, matronly cows,
And tossed the colts' manes all over their brows ;
Till, offended at such an unusual salute,
They all turned their backs, and stood sulky and mute.

So on it went, capering and playing its pranks,—
Whistling with reeds on the broad river's banks,
Puffing the birds as they sat on the spray,
Or the traveller grave on the king's highway.
It was not too nice to hustle the bags
Of the beggar, and flutter his dirty rags ;
'Twas so bold, that it feared not to play its joke
With the doctor's wig or the gentleman's cloak.
Through the forest it roared, and cried gaily, " Now,
You sturdy old oaks, I'll make you bow ! "
And it made them bow without more ado,
Or it cracked their great branches through and
      through.

P.T.O.

Then it rushed like a monster on cottage and farm ;
Striking their dwellers with sudden alarm ;
And they ran out like bees in a midsummer swarm :
There were dames with their kerchiefs tied over their
      caps,
To see if their poultry were free from mishaps ;
The turkeys they gobbled, the geese screamed aloud,
And the hens crept to roost in a terrified crowd ;
There was rearing of ladders, and logs were laid on,
Where the thatch from the roof threatened soon to be
      gone.

But the Wind had swept on, and met in a lane
With a schoolboy, who panted and struggled in vain ;
For it tossed him and twirled him, then passed—and
      he stood
With his hat in a pool and his shoes in the mud !

Then away went the Wind in its holiday glee,
And now it was far on the billowy sea ;
And the lordly ships felt its staggering blow,
And the little boats darted to and fro.

But, lo ! it was night, and it sank to rest
On the sea-birds' rock in the gleaming west,
Laughing to think, in its frolicsome fun,
How little of mischief it really had done.

                              WILLIAM HOWITT.

Is this a poem of to-day ?   How soon do you find out ?
Would the schoolboy be a Boy Scout ?
   Is the line of this poem long or short ?   Do you think
the writer purposely made it so ; and, if so, why ?
   Do the lines step slowly or quickly ?
   What have you noticed about the length of the stanzas ?
   Could a film be made to show the frolics of the wind ?
   What do you understand by " It was not too *nice* " ?
   Try to write another stanza telling what the wind
might have done in your own street or town.   Do not
forget the rhymes for each pair of lines.

When Polly buys a Hat

When Father goes to town with me to buy my
    Sunday hat,
We can't afford to waste much time in doing things
    like that ;
We walk into the nearest shop, and Father tells them
    then,
" Just bring a hat you think will fit a little girl of ten ! "

It may be plain, it may be fine with lace and flowers
    too ;
If it just " feels right " upon my head we think that
    it will do ;
It may be red or brown or blue, with ribbons light or
    dark ;
We put it on—and take the car that goes to Central
    Park.

When Mother buys my hat for me, we choose the shape
    with care ;
We ask if it's the best they have, and if they're sure
    'twill wear ;
And when the trimming's rather fine, why, Mother
    shakes her head
And says, " Please take the feathers off—we'd like a
    bow instead ! "

But oh, when Sister buys my hats, you really do not
    know
The hurry and the worry that we have to undergo !
How many times I've heard her say,—and shivered
    where I sat,—
" I think I'll go to town to-day, and buy that child a
    hat ! "

They bring great hats with curving brims, but I'm too
    tall for those ;
And hats that have no brims at all, which do not suit
    my nose ;
I walk about, and turn around, and struggle not to
    frown ;
And wish I had long curly hair like Angelina Brown.

Till when at last the daylight goes, and I'm so tirèd
    then,
I hope I'll never, never need another hat again,
And when I've quite made up my mind that shopping
    is the worst
Of all my tasks—then Sister buys the hat that we saw
    first !

And so we take it home with us as quickly as we may,
And Sister lifts it from the box and wonders what
    they'll say ;
And I—I peep into the glass, and (promise not to tell !)
I smile, because I really think it suits me very well ;

Then slip into the library as quiet as can be,
And this is what my Brother says when first he looks
    at me :
" Upon—my—word ! I never saw a queerer sight than
    that !
Don't tell me this outrageous thing is Polly's Sunday
    hat ! "

E. HILL.

Now can you begin again with—
" When Father buys himself a hat he walks into the
shop," and go on to tell how he chooses the first, sticks it
on, goes out, nearly loses it in the wind, and has to go back
to the shop to choose one which will fit better ?   Then you
might perhaps deal with Brother buying a hat, or perhaps
a pair of boots, and pay him out for what he said to Polly.

Quote a proverb which explains the idea of the poem.

The line of these verses is long, but it can always be neatly divided. Can you show in each line where the division falls. Write down the first stanza in eight lines.

The Babes in the Wood

Now ponder well, you parents dear,
    These words which I shall write ;
A doleful story you shall hear,
    In time brought forth to light.
A gentleman of good account
    In Norfolk dwelt of late,
Who did in honour far surmount
    Most men of his estate.

Sore sick he was, and like to die,
    No help his life could save ;
His wife by him as sick did lie,
    And both possessed one grave.
No love between these two was lost,
    Each was to other kind ;
In love they lived, in love they died,
    And left two babes behind.

The one a fine and pretty boy,
    Not passing three years old ;
The other a girl more young than he,
    And framed in beauty's mould.
The father left his little son,
    As plainly doth appear,
When he to perfect age should come,
    Three hundred pounds a year.

And to his little daughter, Jane,
    Five hundred pounds in gold,
To be paid down on marriage-day,
    Which might not be controlled.

But if the children chance to die
　　Ere they to age should come,
Their uncle should possess their wealth ;
　　For so the will did run.

" Now, brother," said the dying man,
　　" Look to my children dear ;
Be good unto my boy and girl,
　　No friends else have they here ;
To God and you I recommend
　　My children dear this day ;
But little while be sure we have
　　Within this world to stay.

" You must be father and mother both,
　　And uncle all in one ;
God knows what will become of them
　　When I am dead and gone."
With that bespake their mother dear,
　　" Oh, brother kind," quoth she,
" You are the man must bring our babes
　　To wealth or misery :

" And if you keep them carefully,
　　Then God will you reward ;
But if you otherwise should deal,
　　God will your deeds regard."
With lips as cold as any stone
　　They kissed their children small :
" God bless you both, my children dear ! "
　　With that the tears did fall.

These speeches then their brother spoke,
　　To this sick couple there :
" The keeping of your little ones,
　　Sweet sister, do not fear :

God never prosper me nor mine,
　　Nor ought else that I have,
If I do wrong your children dear,
　　When you are laid in grave."

The parents being dead and gone,
　　The children home he takes,
And brings them straight unto his house,
　　Where much of them he makes.
He had not kept these pretty babes
　　A twelvemonth and a day,
But, for their wealth, he did devise
　　To make them both away.

He bargained with two ruffians strong,
　　Which were of furious mood,
That they should take these children young,
　　And slay them in a wood.
He told his wife an artful tale,
　　He would the children send,
To be brought up in fair London,
　　With one that was his friend.

Away then went those pretty babes
　　Rejoicing at their tide,
Rejoicing in a merry mind,
　　They should on cock-horse ride.
They prate and prattle pleasantly
　　As they rode on the way,
To those that should their butchers be,
　　And work their lives' decay.

So that the pretty speech they had
　　Made Murder's heart relent ;
And they that undertook the deed
　　Full sore did now repent.

Yet one of them more hard of heart
   Did vow to do his charge,
Because the wretch that hired him
   Had paid him very large.

The other won't agree thereto,
   So here they fall to strife ;
With one another they did fight,
   About the children's life ;
And he that was of mildest mood
   Did slay the other there,
Within an unfrequented wood ;
   The babes did quake for fear !

He took the children by the hand,
   Tears standing in their eye,
And bade them straightway follow him
   And look they did not cry.
And two long miles he led them on,
   While they for food complain ;
" Stay here," quoth he ; " I'll bring you bread
   When I come back again."

These pretty babes, with hand in hand,
   Went wandering up and down ;
But never more could see the man
   Approaching from the town :
Their pretty lips with blackberries
   Were all besmeared and dyed ;
And when they saw the darksome night
   They sat them down and cried.

Thus wandered these poor innocents,
   Till death did end their grief ;
In one another's arms they died,
   As wanting due relief.

No burial this pretty pair
    Of any man receives,
Till Robin Redbreast piously
    Did cover them with leaves.

And now the heavy wrath of God
    Upon their uncle fell ;
Yea, fearful fiends did haunt his house,
    His conscience felt an hell :
His barns were fired, his goods consumed,
    His lands were barren made,
His cattle died within the field,
    And nothing with him stayed.

And in a voyage to Portugal
    Two of his sons did die ;
And to conclude, himself was brought
    To want and misery :
He pawned and mortgaged all his land
    Ere seven years came about ;
And now at length this wicked act
    Did by this means come out :

The fellow that did take in hand
    These children for to kill,
Was for a robbery judged to die,
    Such was God's blessed will ;
So did confess the very truth,
    As here hath been displayed ;
Their uncle having died in gaol,
    Where he for debt was laid.

You that executors be made
    And overseers eke
Of children that be fatherless
    And infants mild and meek

Take you example by this thing,
   And yield to each his right,
Lest God with such-like misery
   Your wicked minds requite.

OLD BALLAD.

This is an old friend in verse form, written a long time
ago, when men were hanged for stealing, as we are re-
minded in the last stanza but one ; and when the phrase
" No love was lost between them " meant the opposite
to what it does now.

It is a doleful story which some little children appear
to like, probably because of the robin. It is told in a
doleful way, too, with some ugly words, like *pawned* and
mortgaged, not fit for poetry, and it is good fun to try to
brighten it up. Why not make the robin fetch a cottager
who takes care of the little ones, finds out the wicked
uncle, brings him to the gaol, and, if you choose, to the
gallows ! Try it, and try hard to avoid making "robin"
rhyme with "sobbing," but if you cannot help it, never
mind, for it is done in an old nursery rhyme which every
one knows.

The Spring Walk

WE had a pleasant walk to-day,
Over the hills and far away,
Across the bridge by the water-mill,
By the woodside, and up the hill ;
And if you listen to what I say
I'll tell you what we saw to-day.

Amid a hedge, where the first leaves
   Were peeping from their sheaths so shy,
We saw four eggs within a nest,
   And they were blue as the summer sky.

An elder branch dipped in the brook,
   We wondered why it moved, and found

A silken-haired, smooth water-rat
   Nibbling and swimming round and round.

Where daisies opened to the sun,
   In a broad meadow, green and white,
The lambs were racing eagerly—
   We never saw a prettier sight.

We saw upon the shady banks
   Long rows of golden flowers shine,
And first mistook for buttercups
   The star-shaped yellow celandine.

Anemones and primroses,
   And the blue violets of spring,
We found whilst listening by a hedge
   To hear a merry ploughman sing.

And from the earth the plough turned up
   There came a sweet, refreshing smell,
Such as the lily of the vale
   Sends forth from many a woodland dell.

We saw the yellow wallflower wave
   Upon a mouldering castle wall,
And then we watched the busy rooks
   Among the ancient elm-trees tall.

And leaning from the old stone bridge,
   Below we saw our shadows lie,
And through the gloomy arches watched
   The swift and fearless swallows fly.

We heard the speckle-breasted lark
   As it sang somewhere out of sight ;
And tried to find it, but the sky
   Was filled with clouds of dazzling light.

We saw young rabbits near the wood,
  And heard a pheasant's wing go " whirr " :
And then we saw a squirrel leap
  From an old oak tree to a fir.

We came back by the village fields,
  A pleasant walk it was across them,
For all behind the houses lay
  The orchards red and white with blossom.

Were I to tell you all we saw,
  I'm sure that it would take me hours ;
For the whole landscape was alive
  With bees, and birds, and buds, and flowers.

                                        THOMAS MILLER.

How many stanzas are there in this poem ? How
many separate word pictures ?
Pick out the moving pictures and the still pictures.
Which are the clearest and prettiest ?
Did the people who took this pleasant walk do any
damage on the way ? Do you think they left any paper
or ginger-beer bottles about ?
Which bird laid the blue eggs in the nest in the hedge ?
Finish this sentence : The heaped-up snow was as
white as ——. Now you have made a *simile*.
Would you know an elder tree ? What kind of leaf
has it ? What fruit does it bear ?
About what time was the walk begun ?
How do flowers get high up in a crack of an old wall ?
Where do rooks build ? What is their call ?
Was the water deep or shallow under the old stone
bridge ?
Where the poet writes " shadows " we should now use
" reflections." Would this new word improve the poetry ?
What kinds of trees were in the orchards ?
Try to add two or three stanzas describing other things
that might have been seen by yourself on this walk.

Of St. Francis and the Ass

OUR father, ere he went
Out with his brother, Death,
Smiling and well-content
As a bridegroom goeth,
Sweetly forgiveness prayed
From man or beast whom he
Had ever injurèd
Or burdened needlessly.

" Verily," then said he,
" I crave before I pass,
Forgiveness full and free
Of my little brother, the ass ;
Many a time and oft,
When winds and ways were hot,
He hath borne me cool and soft,
And service grudged me not.

" And once it did betide
There was, unseen of me,
A gall upon his side
That suffered grievously.
And once his manger was
Empty, and bare, and brown.
(Praise God for sweet, dry grass
That Bethlehem folk shook down.)

" Consider, brethren," said he,
" Our little brother, how mild,
How patient, he will be,
Though men are fierce and wild.
His coat is grey and fine,
His eyes are kind with love ;
This little brother of mine
Is gentle as the dove.

" Consider how such an one
Beheld our Saviour born,
And carried him, full-grown,
Through Eastern streets one morn.
For this the Cross is laid
Upon him for a sign.
Greatly is honourèd
This little brother of mine."

And even while he spake,
Down in his stable stall,
His little ass 'gan shake,
And turned its face to the wall.
Down fell the heavy tear,
Its gaze so mournful was,
Fra Leo, standing near,
Pitied the little ass.

That night our father died,
All night the kine did low,
The ass went heavy-eyed
With patient tears and slow,
The very birds on wings
Made mournful cries in the air.
Amen !   All living things
Our father's brethren were.

KATHARINE TYNAN HINKSON.

This is a poem of to-day, but it tells of St. Francis of
Assisi, who lived in Italy about six hundred years ago,
and who was particularly fond of all animals, and espe-
cially of the birds, which he called his brothers and sisters.
He started the Franciscan order of friars, and Fra, or
Brother, Leo was one of his closest companions.   One of
the Brothers is telling this story, and, of course, speaks of
St. Francis as his " father."

Prove from the first stanza that St. Francis was not
afraid of Death.

Is the story told slowly and quietly, or quickly and
vigorously ?   Does the style of telling suit the subject ?

What was St. Francis thinking about when he mentioned Bethlehem ?

Where is the Cross on the ass ?

Look up St. Matthew xxi., verses 1–9, and try to add a stanza or two telling this story ; or try to do the same with St. Luke ii., verses 8–16.

The Fairy Shoemaker

LITTLE cowboy, what have you heard
    Up on the lonely rath's green mound ?
Only the plaintive yellow bird
    Sighing in sultry fields around,
Chary, chary, chary, chee-ee ?
Only the grasshopper and the bee ?
      " Tip-tap, rip-rap,
        Tick-a-tack-too !
    Scarlet leather sewn together,
      This will make a shoe.
    Left, right, pull it tight ;
      Summer days are warm ;
    Underground in winter,
      Laughing at the storm ! "

Lay your ear close to the hill.
　　Do you not catch the tiny clamour,
　　Busy click of an elfin hammer,
Voice of the Lepracaun singing shrill
　　　　As he merrily plies his trade ?
　　　　　　He's a span
　　　　　　And a quarter in height.
　　　　Get him in sight, hold him tight,
　　　　　　And you're a made
　　　　　　　　Man !

You watch your cattle the summer day,
Sup on potatoes, sleep in the hay ;
　　How would you like to roll in your carriage,
　　Look for a duchess's daughter in marriage ?
Seize the shoemaker—then you may !
　　　　" Big boots a-hunting,
　　　　　　Sandals in the hall,
　　　　White for a wedding feast,
　　　　　　Pink for a ball.
　　　　This way, that way,
　　　　　　So we make a shoe ;
　　　　Getting rich every stitch,
　　　　　　Tick-tack-too ! "

Nine-and-ninety treasure crocks
　　This keen miser-fairy hath,
Hid in mountains, woods, and rocks,
　　Ruin and round-tower, cave and rath.
　　And where the cormorants build ;
　　　　　　From times of old
　　　　　　　　Guarded by him,
　　　　　　Each of them filled
　　　　　　　　Full to the brim
　　　　　　　　　　With gold !

I caught him at work one day myself,
　　In the castle ditch where foxglove grows ;
A wrinkled, wizened, and bearded elf,

Spectacles stuck on his pointed nose,
Silver buckles to his hose,
    Leather apron, shoe in his lap.
     " Rip-rap, tip-tap,
       Tick-tack-too !
    (A grasshopper on my cap !
    Away the moth flew.)
    Buskins for a fairy prince,
      Brogues for his son ;
    Pay me well, pay me well,
      When the job is done ! "

The rogue was mine, beyond a doubt ;
    I stared at him, he stared at me.
     " Servant, sir ! " " Humph ! " says he,
And pulled a snuff-box out.
He took a long pinch, looked better pleased,
    The queer little Lepracaun ;
   Offered the box with a dainty grace—
    Pouf ! he flung the dust in my face !
      And while I sneezed,
        Was gone !
            WILLIAM ALLINGHAM.
             (*With acknowledgments.*)

Does this poem tell a story or relate an incident ?
Is there anything in this poem that shows you which
country it tells you about ?
How does any one " ply his trade " ?
Measure the length of a span and a quarter.
The third stanza tells you what is meant by " you're a
made man." Where do the cormorants build ?
What is the clearest picture in the poem ?
Can you offer anything to your teacher " with a dainty
grace " ?
How does the stanza of this poem differ in shape, etc.,
from those of other poems you have read, say that of
St. Francis and the Ass ?

The Magpie's Nest

WHEN the arts in their infancy were,
  In a fable of old 'tis exprest,
A wise magpie constructed that rare
  Little house for young birds called a nest.

This was talked of the whole country round,
  You might hear it on every bough sung,
" Now no longer upon the rough ground
  Will fond mothers brood over their young.

" For the magpie with exquisite skill
  Has invented a moss-coloured cell,
Within which a whole family will
  In the utmost security dwell."

To her mate did each female bird say,
  " Let us fly to the magpie, my dear ;
If she will but teach us the way,
  A nest we will build us up here.

" It's a thing that's close arched overhead,
  With a hole made to creep out and in ;
We, my bird, might make just such a bed,
  If we only knew how to begin."

To the magpie soon every bird went,
  And in modest terms made their request,
That she would be pleased to consent
  To teach them to build up a nest.

She replied, " I will show you the way,
  So observe everything that I do.
First two sticks o'er each other I lay "—
  " To be sure," said the crow ; " why, I knew

" It must be begun with two sticks,
  And I thought that they crossèd should be."
Said the pie, " Then some straw and moss mix,
  In the way you now see done by me."

" Oh yes, certainly," said the jackdaw,
  " That must follow of course, I have thought ;
Though I never before building saw,
  I guessed that without being taught."

" More moss, straw, and feathers I place
  In this manner," continued the pie.
" Yes, no doubt, madam, that is the case ;
  Though no builder myself, even I,"—

Said the starling, " I guessed that 'twas so ;
  It must of necessity follow :
For more moss, straw, and feathers, I know,
  It requires to be soft, round, and hollow."

Whatever she taught them beside,
  In his turn every bird of them said,
Though the nest-making art he ne'er tried,
  He had just such a thought in his head !

Still the pie went on showing her art,
  Till a nest she had built up half-way ;
She no more of her skill would impart,
  But in anger went fluttering away.

And this speech in their hearing she made,
  As she perched o'er their heads on a tree,
" If you all were well skilled in my trade,
  Pray, why came you to learn it of me ? "—

When a scholar is willing to learn,
  He with silent submission should hear.
Too late they their folly discern ;
  The effect to this day does appear ;

For whenever a pie's nest you see,
　　Her charming warm canopy view ;
All birds' nests but hers seem to be
　　A magpie's nest just cut in two.

CHARLES AND MARY LAMB.

This is an old Nature legend put into rather halting,
and bumping, and stumbling verses.　There is a halt at
the end of line 3 of stanza 1, and a double bump at the
end of line 2 in stanza 2 ; another rough place at the end
of line 3 of stanza 3.　And there are several others, some
of which you may be able to find for yourselves.

Try to mend the third line of stanza 9 by rearranging
the words and still keeping the rhyme with jack*daw*.
Try also to mend line 2 of stanza 12.

Read the poem aloud, and then say which stanzas read
most smoothly.

The lines were written by two famous writers of whom
you will learn more later.

A Maiden came gliding

A MAIDEN came gliding over the sea
In a boat as light as boat could be,
And she sang in tones so sweet and free,
" Oh, where is the youth that will follow me ? "

Her forehead was white as the pearly shell,
Her form was finer than tongue can tell,
Her bosom heaved with a gentle swell,
And her voice was a distant vesper-bell.

And still she sang, while the western light
Fell on her figure so soft and bright,
" Oh, where shall I find the brave young sprite
That will follow the track of my boat to-night ? "

To the strand the youths of the village run,
When the witching song had scarce begun,

And ere the set of that evening's sun,
Fifteen bold lovers the maid has won.

They hoisted the sail, and they plied the oar,
And away they went from their native shore,
While the damsel's pinnace flew fast before,
But never, oh, never ! we saw them more.

JOHN STERLING.

What three parts or separate scenes are there in this little story ?

Study the epithets or descriptive words, such as *pearly* shell, etc. ; also the similes or likenesses, such as " white as the pearly shell," criticizing their aptness or fitness.

Is the poem written in a dancing or slow metre ? Is there any change in the " time " when we come to the last stanza ?

Where do the accents or stresses fall in each line ?

Of which other poem in this book does this one remind you, and how does it differ from it ?

Robin Hood and Alan-a-Dale

[Here is a very old story-poem known as a *ballad*. No one knows who made it up. The few words in the margin explain words not now in use.]

COME listen to me, you gallants so free,
    All you that love mirth for to hear,
And I will tell you of a bold outlaw
    That lived in Nottinghamshire.

As Robin Hood in the forest stood,
    All under the greenwood tree,
He was aware of a brave young man,
    As fine as fine might be.

The youngster was clothed in scarlet red,
    In scarlet fine and gay,

And he did frisk it over the plain,
  And chanted a roundelay.

As Robin Hood next morning stood,
  Amongst the leaves so gay,
There did he espy the same young man
  Come drooping along the way.

The scarlet he wore the day before,
  It was clean cast away ;
And every step he fetched a sigh,
  " Alack and a well-a-day ! "

Then steppèd forth brave Little John
  And Much the miller's son,
Which made the young man bend his bow,
  When as he saw them come.

" Stand off, stand off ! " the young man said,
  " What is your will with me ? "—
" You must come before our master straight,
  Under yon greenwood tree.

And when he came bold Robin before,
  Robin asked him courteously,
" Oh, hast thou any money to spare,
  For my merry men and me ? "

" I have no money," the young man said,
  " But five shillings and a ring ;
And that I have kept these seven long years,
  To have it at my wedding.

" Yesterday I should have married a maid,
  But she is now from me ta'en,
And chosen to be an old knight's delight,
  Whereby my poor heart is slain."

" What is thy name ? " then said Robin Hood,
  " Come tell me without any fail."—
" By the faith of my body," then said the young man,
  " My name it is Alan-a-Dale."

" What wilt thou give me," said Robin Hood,
  " In ready gold or fee,
To help thee to thy true-love again,
  And deliver her unto thee ? "

" I have no money," then quoth the young man,
  " No ready gold nor fee,
But I will swear upon a book
  Thy true servant for to be."—

" But how many miles to thy true-love ?
  Come tell me without any guile."—
" By the faith of my body," then said the young man,
  " It is but five little mile."

Then Robin he hasted over the plain,
  He did neither stint nor lin,   *delay nor stop*
Until he came unto the church
  Where Alan should keep his wedding.

" What dost thou do here ? " the Bishop he said,
  " I prithee now tell to me : "
" I am a bold harper," quoth Robin Hood,
  And the best in the north countrie."

" Oh, welcome, oh, welcome ! " the Bishop he said,
  " That music best pleaseth me."—
" You shall have no music," quoth Robin Hood,
  " Till the bride and the bridegroom I see."

With that came in a wealthy knight,
  Which was both grave and old,
And after him a finikin lass,   *neat, dainty*
  Did shine like glistering gold.

" This is no fit match," quoth bold Robin Hood,
  " That you do seem to make here ;
For since we are come unto the church,
  The bride she shall choose her own dear."

Then Robin Hood put his horn to his mouth,
  And blew blasts two or three ;
When four-and-twenty bowmen bold
  Came leaping over the lee.

And when they came into the churchyard,
  Marching all on a row,
The first man was Alan-a-Dale,
  To give bold Robin his bow.

" This is thy true-love," Robin he said,
  " Young Alan, as I hear say ;
And you shall be married at this same time,
  Before we depart away."

" That shall not be," the Bishop he said,
  " For thy word it shall not stand ;
They shall be three times asked in the church,
  As the law is of our land."

Robin Hood pulled off the Bishop's coat,
  And put it upon Little John ;
" By the faith of my body," then Robin said,
  "This cloth doth make thee a man."

When Little John went into the quire,
  The people began for to laugh ;
He asked them seven times in the church,
  Lest three should not be enough.

" Who gives me this maid ? " then said Little John ;
  Quoth Robin, " That do I !
And he that doth take her from Alan-a-dale
  Full dearly he shall her buy."

And thus having ended this merry wedding,
   The bride she looked like a queen,
And so they returned to the merry greenwood,
   Amongst the leaves so green.

OLD BALLAD.

How did the first teller of this story probably pronounce
" Nottinghamshire " ?

How did the outlaws support themselves ? What
would happen to them if the sheriff's men caught them ?

Note that Little John was a priest, though he was
" unfrocked "—that is, he was no longer allowed to act as
a priest.

Select the best pictures in this story, and describe each
one briefly.

Read the line which shows that the bride was well
pleased with the new bridegroom.

This poem makes a good little play. Try it.

Earl Mar's Daughter

[This old story-poem or ballad comes from Scotland,
and contains a few words which may be strange to you,
but you will find them explained in the margin.]

IT was intill a pleasant time,   *once*
   Upon a summer's day,
The noble Earl Mar's daughter
   Went forth to sport and play.

And as she played and sported
   Below a green oak tree,
There she saw a sprightly doo   *dove*
   Set on a branch so hie.   *high*

" O Coo-my-doo, my Love so true,
   If ye'll come down to me,
Ye'll have a cage of good red gold
   Instead o' simple tree.

" I'll put gold hingers roun' your cage,
    And siller round your wa',   *silver*
I'll gar ye shine as fair a bird   *make*
    As any o' them a'."

And she had not these words well spoke,
    Nor yet these words well said,
Till Coo-my-doo flew from the tower
    And lighted on her head.

Then she has brought this pretty bird
    Home to her bower and ha',
And made him shine as fair a bird
    As any o' them a'.

When day was gone and night was come,
    About the evening-tide,
This lady spied a sprightly youth
    Stand straight up by her side.

" Oh, who are ye, young man ? " she said,
    " What country come ye frae ? "—   *from*
" I flew across the sea," he said,
    " 'Twas but this very day.

" My mither is a queen," he says,
    " Likewise of magic skill ;
'Twas she that turned me to a doo,
    To fly where'er I will.

" And it was but this very day
    That I came o'er the sea :
I loved you at a single look ;
    With you I'll live and dee."—

" O Coo-my-doo, my Love so true,
    No more from me ye'll gae—"   *go*
" That's never my intent, my Love :
    As ye said, it shall be sae."   *so*

Thus he has stayed in bower with her
    For twenty years and three ;
Till there came a lord of high renown
    To court this fair ladye.

But still his proffer she refused,
    And all his presents too ;
Says, " I'm content to live alone
    With my bird Coo-my-doo."

Her father sware a solemn oath,
    Among the nobles all,
" To-morrow, ere I eat or drink,
    That bird I'll surely kill."

The bird was sitting in his cage,
    And heard what he did say ;
He jumped upon the window-sill :
    " 'Tis time I was away."

Then Coo-my-doo took flight and flew
    Beyond the raging sea,
And lighted at his mother's castle,
    On a tower of gold so hie.

The Queen his mother was walking out,
    To see what she could see,
And there she saw her darling son
    Set on the tower so hie.

" Get dancers here to dance," she said,
    " And minstrels for to play ;
For here's my dear son Florentine
    Come hame wi' me to stay."—

" Instead of dancers to dance, mither,
    Or minstrels for to play,
Turn four-and-twenty well-wight men   *strong*
    Like storks, in feathers grey ;

" My seven sons to seven swans,
  Above their heads to flee ;
And I myself a gay goshawk,
  A bird o' high degree."

This flock of birds took flight and flew
  Beyond the raging sea ;
They landed near the Earl Mar's castle,
  Took shelter in every tree.

These birds flew up from bush and tree,
  And lighted on the ha' ;
And when the wedding-train came forth
  Flew down among them a'.

The storks they seized each wedding guest,
  That they could not fight or flee ;
The swans they bound the bridegroom fast
  Unto a green oak tree.

They lighted next on the bride-maidens,
  Then on the bride's own head ;
And with the twinkling of an e'e,   *eye*
  The bride an' them were fled !

There's ancient men at weddings been
  For sixty years or more,
But siccan a curious wedding day   *such*
  They never saw before.

For naething could the companie do,
  And naething could they say ;
But they saw a flock o' pretty birds
  That took their bride away.

                                        OLD BALLAD.

Some of the best ballads come from Scotland, and most
of the creepy ones with witches, and magic, and murders,
and fights in them.   These old story-poems were made

up long before books were printed, and were sung or
recited by the fire on winter evenings.

Which do you consider the most musical lines in this
poem ?

The old story-tellers sometimes left out part of the
story.

Which part of this tale is not made quite clear ?

Which is the prettiest picture in the story ?

The Water o' Wearie's Well

THERE came a bird out of a bush,
    On water for to dine,
An sighing sair, says the king's daughter,   *sorely*
    " Oh, wae's this heart o' mine ! "

He's ta'en a harp into his hand,
    He's harped them all asleep,
Except it was the king's daughter,
    Who one wink couldna get.

He's luppen on his berry-brown steed,   *leapt*
    Ta'en her on behind himsell,
Then baith rede down to that water   *rode*
    That they ca' Wearie's Well.

" Wide in, wide in, my lady fair,   *wade*
    No harm shall thee befall ;
Oft times I've waterèd my steed
    Wi' the water o' Wearie's Well."

The first step that she steppèd in,
    She steppèd to the knee ;
And sighend says this lady fair,   *sighing*
    " This water's nae for me."

" Wide in, wide in, my lady fair,
    No harm shall thee befall ;
Oft times I've waterèd my steed
    Wi' the water o' Wearie's Well."

The next step that she steppèd in,
   She steppèd to the middle ;
" Oh," sighend says this lady fair,
   " I've wat my gowden girdle."   *wet*

" Wide in, wide in, my lady fair,
   No harm shall thee befall ;
Oft times have I waterèd my steed
   Wi' the water o' Wearie's Well."

The next step that she steppèd in,
   She steppèd to the chin ;
" Oh," sighend says this lady fair,
   " They sud gar twa loves twin ! "   *make separate*

" Seven kings' daughters I've drownèd there,
   In the water o' Wearie's Well,
And I'll make you the eight o' them,
   And ring the common bell."

" Since I am standing here," she says,
   " This dowie death to die,   *sad*
One kiss o' your comely mouth
   I'm sure wad comfort me."

He louted him o'er his saddle-bow,   *leant* or *bowed*
   To kiss her cheek and chin ;
She's ta'en him in her arms twa,
   And thrown him headlong in.

" Since seven kings' daughter ye've drownèd there,
   In the water o' Wearie's Well,
I'll make you bridegroom to them a',
   An ring the bell mysell."

And aye she warsled, and aye she swam,   *struggled*
   And she swam to dry lan' ;
She thankèd God most cheerfully
   The dangers she o'ercame.

                      OLD BALLAD.

What is there which is abrupt about the first part of this very old ballad ?

Perhaps the first person who wrote it down missed out a stanza after " heart o' mine." Try to make it up, telling how the bird changed into a knight who followed the maiden to her father's castle.

What is your verdict on this story ?

Allison Gross

O ALLISON GROSS, that lives in yon tower,
    The ugliest witch in the north countrie,
Has trysted me ae day up till her bower,   *met me at*
    And mony fair speech she made to me.

She stroked my head, an she kembed my hair, *combed*
    An she set me down saftiy on her knee ;
Says, " Gin ye will be my luver so true,   *if*
    Sae mony braw things as I would you gi'e." *fine*

She showed me a mantle o' red scarlet,
    Wi' gouden flowrs an fringes fine ;   *golden*
Says, " Gin ye will be my luver so true,
    This goodly gift it sal be thine."

" Awa, awa, ye ugly witch,
    Haud far awa, an lat me be ;   *keep off*
I never will be your luver sae true,
    An I wish I were out o' your company."

She neist brought a sark o' the saftest silk,   *shirt*
    Well wrought wi' pearles about the ban ; *neck*
Says, " Gin you will be my ain true love,
    This goodly gift you sal comman."

She showed me a cup of the good red gold,
    Well set wi' jewls sae fair to see ;
Says, " Gin you will be my luver sae true,
    This goodly gift I will you gi'e."

" Awa, awa, ye ugly witch,
  Haud far awa, an lat me be ;
For I wouldna ance kiss your ugly mouth
  For a' the gifts that ye could gi'e."

She's turned her right and round about,
  An thrice she blaw on a grass-green horn,
An she sware by the moon and the stars aboon,
  That she'd gar me rue the day I was born.   *make*

Then out has she ta'en a silver wand,
  An she's turned her three times round and round ;
She's muttered sich words till my strength it failed,
  An I fell down senseless upon the ground.

She's turned me into an ugly worm,
  And gar'd me writhle about the tree ;
An ay, on ilka Saturday's night,   *each*
  My sister Maisry came to me,

Wi' silver bason an silver kemb,   *comb*
  To kemb my heady upon her knee ;
But or I had kissed her ugly mouth,   *before*
  I'd rather ha' writhled about the tree.

But as it fell out on last Hallow-even,
  When the seely court was ridin' by,   *fairy*
The queen lighted down on a gowany bank,   *daisied*
  Nae far frae the tree where I wont to lye.   *used*

She took me up in her milk-white han,
  An she's stroked me three times o'er her knee ;
She changed me again to my ain proper shape,
  An I nae mair maun writhle about the tree.   *must*

                                   OLD BALLAD.

The old ballad often repeats words and phrases. What
examples of this kind of repetition can you find in the
ballads you have just read ?

So far, our ballads have all been in stanzas of four lines, each with two lines ending in the same sound. Try to put the following story, or even a portion of it, into stanzas of this kind :

There was once a very great and wise king, who ruled in a land far away.

No one could ask him a question that he was not able to answer. He could tell all about animals and plants.

Now a certain queen heard of him, and thought she would try to puzzle him. So she picked a bunch of clover, and had the flowers and leaves copied in wax.

When this had been done the queen herself could not tell the real clover from the wax clover. Nor could any one else.

Then she took them to the king, so that he might tell which was wax and which was real.

The king soon found out a way. He placed the flowers near the bee-hive in his garden.

To which bunch did the bees fly ?

King Lear and his Three Daughters

KING LEAR once rulèd in this land
    With princely power and peace ;
And had all things with heart's content,
    That might his joys increase.
Amongst those things that Nature gave,
    Three daughters fair had he,
So princely seeming, beautiful,
    As fairer could not be.

So on a time it pleased the king
    A question thus to move,
Which of his daughters to his grace
    Could show the dearest love :
" For to my age you bring content,"
    Quoth he, " then let me hear
Which of you three in plighted troth
    The kindest will appear."

To whom the eldest thus began :
    " Dear father mine," quoth she,
" Before your face to do you good,
    My blood shall rendered be :
And for your sake my bleeding heart
    Shall here be cut in twain,
Ere that I see your reverend age
    The smallest grief sustain."

" And so will I," the second said ;
    " Dear father, for your sake,
The worst of all extremities
    I'll gently undertake :
And serve your highness night and day
    With diligence and love ;
That sweet content and quietness
    Discomforts may remove."

" In doing so, you glad my soul,"
    The agèd king replied ;
" What sayest thou, my youngest girl,
    How is thy love ally'd ? "
" *My love*," quoth young Cordelia then,
    " *Which to your grace I owe,*
Shall be the duty of a child,
    And that is all I'll show."

" And wilt thou show no more," quoth he,
    " Than doth thy duty bind ?
I well perceive thy love is small,
    When as no more I find.
Henceforth I banish thee my court,
    Thou art no child of mine ;
Nor any part of this my realm
    By favour shall be thine.

" Thy elder sisters' loves are more
    Than I can well demand,

On whom I equally bestow
  My kingdom and my land,
My royal state and all my goods,
  That lovingly I may
With those thy sisters be maintained
  Until my dying day."

Thus flattering speeches won renown
  By these two sisters here ;
The third had causeless banishment,
  Yet was her love more dear :
For poor Cordelia patiently
  Went wand'ring up and down,
Unhelped, unpitied, gentle maid,
  Through many an English town.

Until at last in famous France
  She gentler fortunes found ;
Though poor and meek, yet she was deemed
  The fairest on the ground :
Where, when the king her virtues heard,
  And had this lady seen,
With full consent of all his court,
  He made his wife and queen.

Her father, old King Lear, this while
  With his two daughters stayed :
Forgetful of their promised loves,
  Full soon the same decayed ;
For living in Queen Regan's court,
  The elder of the twain,
She took from him his chiefest means,
  And most of all his train.

For whereas twenty men were wont
  To wait with bended knee,
She gave allowance but to ten,
  And after scarce to three ;

Nay, one she thought too much for him,
   So took she all away,
In hope that in her court, good king,
   He would no longer stay.

" Am I rewarded thus," quoth he,
   " In giving all I have
Unto my children, and to beg
   For what I lately gave ?
I'll go unto my Gonorell :
   My second child, I know,
Will be more kind and pitiful,
   And will remove my woe."

Full fast he hies then to her court ;
   Who, when she heard his moan,
Returned him answer, that she grieved
   That all his means were gone ;
But no way could relieve his wants ;
   Yet, if that he would stay
Within her kitchen, he should have
   What scullions gave away.

When he had heard with bitter tears,
   He made his answer then :
" In what I did, let me be made
   Example to all men.
I will return again," quoth he,
   " Unto my Regan's court ;
She will not use me thus, I hope,
   But in a kinder sort."

Where when he came she gave command,
   To drive him thence away :
When he was well within her court
   (She said) he would not stay.
Then back again to Gonorell
   The woeful king did hie,

That in her kitchen he might have
  What scullion boys set by.

But there of that he was denied,
  Which she hath promised late ;
For once refusing, he should not
  Come after to her gate.
Thus 'twixt his daughters for relief
  He wandered up and down ;
Being glad to feed on beggar's food,
  That lately wore a crown.

And calling to remembrance then
  His youngest daughter's words,
That said the duty of a child
  Was all that love affords ;
But doubting to repair to her
  Whom he had banished so,
Grew frantic mad ; for in his mind
  He bore the wounds of woe :

Which made him rend his milk-white locks
  And tresses from his head,
And all with blood bestain his cheeks,
  With age and honour spread.
To hills and woods and watery founts
  He made his hourly moan,
Till hills and woods and senseless things
  Did seem to sigh and groan.

Even thus possessed with discontents,
  He passèd o'er to France,
In hopes from fair Cordelia there
  To find some gentler chance ;
Most virtuous dame ! who when she heard
  Of this her father's grief,
As duty bound she quickly sent
  Him comfort and relief :

And by a train of noble peers,
    In brave and gallant sort,
She gave in charge he should be brought
    Unto her husband's court ;
This royal king with noble mind
    So freely gave consent
To muster up his knights at arms,
    To fame and courage bent.

And so to England came with speed,
    To repossess King Lear,
And drive his daughters from their thrones
    By his Cordelia dear.
Where she, true-hearted, noble queen,
    Was in the battle slain ;
Yet he, good king, in his old days,
    Possessed his crown again.

But when he heard Cordelia's death,
    Who died indeed for love
Of her dear father, in whose cause
    She did this battle move,
He swooning fell upon her breast,
    From whence he never parted :
But on her bosom left his life,
    That was so truly hearted.

                                        OLD BALLAD.

This is an old story used by Shakespeare in one of his
famous plays.

Consider carefully once more the lines printed in italics
in the fifth stanza. This speech seems curt and unkind,
and it is not surprising that the king was angry at it.
Why do you think the gentle-hearted Cordelia spoke in
this way ?

What do you think of the king's question which caused
all the trouble ?

What was Cordelia's real idea of " the duty of a
child " ?

There is a gap in the story after the seventh stanza ; at all events this part of the tale is told in a hurried manner. Try to write another stanza giving the king's sentence upon Cordelia, beginning :

" But as for thee, ungrateful child (or maid),
    It is my firm decree."

Sir Francis Drake, or Eighty-eight

SOME years of late, in eighty-eight,
    As well I do remember a ;
It was, some say, on the ninth of May,
    And some say in September a.

The Spanish train launched forth amain,
    With many a fine bravado ;
Whereas they thought, but it proved nought,
    The Invincible Armado.

There was a little man that dwelt in Spain,
    That shot well in a gun a ;
Don Pedro hight, as black a wight,   *called, . . . man*
    As the knight of the sun a.

King Philip made him admiral,
    And bade him not to stay a ;
But to destroy both man and boy,
    And so to come away a.

The Queen was then at Tilbury,
    What could we more desire a ;
Sir Francis Drake for her sweet sake,
    Did set 'em all on fire a.

Away they ran by sea and land,
    So that one man slew three-score a ;
And had not they all run away,
    O my soul, we had killed more a.   *on*

Then let them neither brag nor boast,
    For if they come again a,
Let them take heed they do not speed,
    As they did they knew when a.

OLD BALLAD.

This is a curious old song of Armada times, very rough, and by no means clear, but full of spirit.

Some of the stanzas seem to be missing.   Try to make a new one to follow the fourth; then another after the sixth stanza to tell how the storm helped the English sailors to defeat the Armada (see any history book).

Kathleen

O NORAH, lay your basket down
    And rest your weary hand,
And come and hear me sing a song
    Of our old Ireland.

There was a lord of Galloway,
    A mighty lord was he;
And he did wed a second wife,
    A maid of low degree.

But he was old, and she was young,
    And so, in evil spite,
She baked the black bread for his kin,
    And fed her own with white.

She whipped the maids and starved the kern,
    And drove away the poor;
" Ah, woe is me ! " the old lord said;
    " I rue my bargain sore ! "

This lord he had a daughter fair,
    Beloved of old and young,
And nightly round the shealing-fires
    Of her the gleeman sung.

" As sweet and good is young Kathleen
   As Eve before her Fall ; "
So sang the harper at the fair,
   So harped he in the hall.

" Oh, come to me, my daughter dear !
   Come sit upon my knee :
For looking in your face, Kathleen,
   Your mother's own I see ! "

He smoothed and smoothed her hair away,
   He kissed her forehead fair ;
" It is my darling Mary's brow,
   It is my darling's hair ! "

Oh, then spake up the angry dame,
   " Get up, get up," quoth she ;
" I'll sell ye over Ireland,
   I'll sell ye o'er the sea ! "

She clipped her glossy hair away,
   That none her rank might know ;
She took away her gown of silk,
   And gave her one of tow ;

And sent her down to Limerick town,
   And to a seaman sold
This daughter of an Irish lord
   For ten good pounds in gold.

The lord he smote upon his breast,
   And tore his beard so grey ;
But he was old, and she was young,
   And so she had her way.

Sure, that same night the Banshee howled
   To fright the evil dame,
And fairy folks, who loved Kathleen,
   With funeral torches came.

She watched them glancing through the trees,
    And glimmering down the hill ;
They crept before the dead-vault door,
    And there they all stood still !

" Get up, old man ! the wake-lights shine ! "
    " Ye wicked witch," quoth he,
" So I'm rid of your tongue, I little care
    If they shine for you or me.

" Oh, whoso brings my daughter back,
    My gold and land shall have ! "
Oh, then spake up his handsome page :
    " No gold nor land I crave !

" But give to me your daughter dear,
    Give sweet Kathleen to me ;
Be she on sea or be she on land,
    I'll bring her back to thee."

" My daughter is a lady born,
    And you of low degree ;
But she shall be your bride the day
    You bring her back to me."

He sailèd east, he sailèd west,
    And far and long sailed he,
Until he came to Boston town,
    Across the great salt sea.

" Oh, have ye seen the young Kathleen,
    The flower of Ireland ?
Ye'll know her by her eyes so blue,
    And by her snow-white hand ! "

Out spake an ancient man : " I know
    The maiden whom ye mean ;
I bought her of a Limerick man,
    And she is called Kathleen.

" No skill hath she in household work,
    Her hands are soft and white,
Yet well by loving looks and ways
    She doth her cost requite."

So up they walked through Boston town,
    And met a maiden fair,
A little basket on her arm
    So snowy-white and bare.

" Come hither, child, and say hast thou
    This young man ever seen ? "
They wept within each other's arms,
    The page and young Kathleen.

" Oh, give to me this darling child,
    And take my purse of gold."
" Nay, not by me," her master said,
    " Shall sweet Kathleen be sold.

" We loved her in the place of one
    The Lord hath early ta'en ;
But since her heart's in Ireland,
    We give her back again ! "

Sure, now they dwell in Ireland ;
    As you go up Claremore,
Ye'll see their castle looking down
    The pleasant Galway shore.

And the old lord's wife is dead and gone,
    And a happy man is he,
For he sits beside his own Kathleen,
    With her darling on his knee.

JOHN G. WHITTIER.

Many poets of our own time have tried to write ballads
like the old ones, and this is one written by an American
poet who lived not very long ago.

In what way or ways has he copied the old ballads ?
(Think both of the story and of the lines and stanzas.)

Is his story one of magic, or a simple tale of things
that might have happened ?   Has it a happy or a sad
ending ?

Of which well-known nursery tale does the story, in
some ways, remind you ?

What is your opinion of the character of the lord of
Galloway ?

People were really sold into slavery at this time, as
you will find out when you read a fine story called *Hereward the Wake*, by Charles Kingsley.

Shameful Death

THERE were four of us about that bed ;
　　The mass-priest knelt at the side,
I and his mother stood at the head,
　　Over his feet lay the bride ;
We were quite sure that he was dead,
　　Though his eyes were open wide.

He did not die in the night,
　　He did not die in the day,
But in the morning twilight
　　His spirit passed away,
When neither sun nor moon was bright,
　　And the trees were merely grey.

He was not slain with the sword,
　　Knight's axe, or the knightly spear,
Yet spoke he never a word
　　After he came in here ;
I cut away the cord
　　From the neck of my brother dear.

He did not strike one blow,
　　For the recreants came behind,

In a place where the hornbeams grow,
   A path right hard to find,
For the hornbeam boughs swing so,
   That the twilight makes it blind.

They lighted a great torch then,
   When his arms were pinioned fast,
Sir John the knight of the Fen,
   Sir Guy of the Dolorous Blast,
With knights threescore and ten,
   Hung brave Lord Hugh at last.

I am threescore and ten,
   And my hair is all turned grey,
But I met Sir John of the Fen
   Long ago on a summer day,
And am glad to think of the moment when
   I took his life away.

I am threescore and ten,
   And my strength is mostly passed,
But long ago I and my men,
   When the sky was overcast,
And the smoke rolled over the reeds of the fen,
   Slew Guy of the Dolorous Blast.

And now, knights all of you,
   I pray you pray for Sir Hugh,
A good knight and a true,
   And for Alice his wife pray too.

W. Morris.

This poem is also a copy of the old ballads, written by a poet who died not very long ago. In what way, or ways, has the poet copied them ?

Who is supposed to be telling the story ? Note how he is too much ashamed to say at first how Lord Hugh had died.

Would he have revenged him if he had been slain in a fair fight ?

The poet can make good word-pictures. Which do you think the best of them ?

In which part of England did these people live ?

A Legend of Bregenz

GIRT round with rugged mountains
    The fair Lake Constance lies ;
In her blue heart reflected,
    Shine back the starry skies ;
And watching each white cloudlet
    Float silently and slow,
You think a piece of heaven
    Lies on our earth below.

Midnight is there : and Silence,
    Enthroned in heaven, looks down
Upon her own calm mirror,
    Upon a sleeping town ;
For Bregenz, that quaint city
    Upon the Tyrol shore,
Has stood above Lake Constance
    A thousand years and more.

Her battlements and towers
    Upon their rocky steep
Have cast their trembling shadow
    For ages on the deep ;
Mountain and lake and valley
    A sacred legend know,
Of how the town was saved one night
    Three hundred years ago.

Far from her home and kindred
    A Tyrol maid had fled,
To serve in the Swiss valleys,
    And toil for daily bread ;

Which lines in the poem
suit this picture?

And every year that fleeted
   So silently and fast
Seemed to bear farther from her
   The memory of the past.

She spoke no more of Bregenz
   With longing and with tears ;
Her Tyrol home seemed faded
   In a deep mist of years.
She heeded not the rumours
   Of Austrian war and strife ;
Each day she rose contented
   To the calm toils of life.

Yet, when her master's children
   Would clustering round her stand,
She sang them the old ballads
   Of her own native land ;
And when at morn and evening
   She knelt before God's throne,
The accents of her childhood
   Rose to her lips alone.

And so she dwelt : the valley
   More peaceful year by year ;
When suddenly strange portents
   Of some great deed seemed near.
One day, out in the meadow,
   With strangers from the town,
Some secret plan discussing,
   The men walked up and down.

At eve they all assembled,
   All care and doubt were fled,
With jovial laugh they feasted,
   The board was nobly spread.

The elder of the village
  Rose up, his glass in hand,
And cried, " We drink the downfall
  Of an accursèd land !

" The night is growing darker—
  Ere one more day is flown,
Bregenz, our foeman's stronghold,
  Bregenz shall be our own ! "
The women shrank in terror
  (Yet Pride, too, had her part),
But one poor Tyrol maiden
  Felt death within her heart.

Nothing she heard around her
  (Though shouts rang forth again) ;
Gone were the green Swiss valleys,
  The pasture, and the plain ;
Before her eyes one vision,
  And in her heart one cry,
That said, " Go forth, save Bregenz ;
  And then, if need be, die ! "

With trembling haste and breathless
  With noiseless step she sped—
Horses and weary cattle
  Were standing in the shed.
She loosed the strong white charger
  That fed from out her hand ;
She mounted, and she turned his head
  Toward her native land.

Out—out into the darkness—
  Faster, and still more fast ;
The smooth grass flies behind her,
  The chestnut wood is past.

She looks up : clouds are heavy ;—
    Why is her steed so slow ?—
Scarcely the wind beside them
    Can pass them as they go.

" Faster ! " she cries, " oh, faster ! "
    Eleven the church-bells chime ;
" O God," she cries, " help Bregenz,
    And bring me there in time ! "
But louder than bells' ringing,
    Or lowing of the kine,
Grows nearer in the midnight
    The rushing of the Rhine.

She strives to pierce the blackness,
    And looser throws the rein ;
Her steed must breast the waters
    That dash above his mane.
How gallantly, how nobly,
    He struggles through the foam !
And see, in the far distance
    Shine out the lights of home !

Up the steep bank he bears her,
    And now they rush again
Towards the heights of Bregenz,
    That tower above the plain.
They reach the gate of Bregenz
    Just as the midnight rings,
And out come serf and soldier
    To meet the news she brings.

Bregenz is saved !—ere daylight
    Her battlements are manned ;
Defiance greets the army
    That marches on the land.
And if to deeds heroic
    Should endless fame be paid,

Bregenz does well to honour
   The noble Tyrol maid.

Three hundred years are vanished,
   And yet upon the hill
An old stone gateway rises
   To do her honour still.
And there, when Bregenz women
   Sit spinning in the shade,
They see in quaint old carving
   The charger and the maid.

And when, to guard old Bregenz,
   By gateway, street, and tower,
The warder paces all night long,
   And calls each passing hour—
" Nine," " ten," " eleven," he cries aloud,
   And then (O crown of Fame !)
When midnight pauses in the skies,
   He calls the maiden's name !

ADELAIDE A. PROCTER.

Is the line of this poem slower or quicker than that of
King Lear ?   Can you find a reason ?

The writer has chosen an old story.   Has she treated
it in the old ballad way ?   Why do you think so ?

A Ballad of St. Christopher

THERE dwelt at the court of a good king
    A giant huge and black,
He could take up Gedney church
    And carry it on his back ;
A giant fierce and grim as he
No king had in his giantry.

This paynim wight was dull of wit,
    But he held fast one thing,
That the strongest man in all the world
    Should serve the strongest king,
A purpose firm he had in mind,
The mightiest king on earth to find.

A minstrel sang a song of the Devil.
    The giant gasped to see
That the king made at the Devil's name
    A sign with fingers three.
" Ho ! ho ! " said the giant, " I stay not here
To serve a king who goes in fear."

The giant found the great black Devil,
    And bid him homage true,
To be his faithful bondservant,
    His bidding aye to do ;
With his new master night and morn
He fired farmsteads and trampled corn.

They went on a lonely road one day,
    Plotting great harm and loss ;
" I must turn back," the Devil said sudden,
    " For here I see a Cross."
" Ho ! ho ! " said the giant, " is here the sign
Of a king whose power is more than thine ? "

" Gallows of God ! " the Devil said,
   And white with rage went he,
" He took the gallows for Himself,
   That, sure, belonged to me ;
He took the gallows, He took the thief,
He stole my harvest sheaf by sheaf.

" He broke my gates, He harried my realm,
   He freed my prisoned folk,
He crowned His Mother for Eve discrowned,
   My kingdom went like smoke ;
Where'er I go by night or day
That sign has power to bar my way.

" Great is my might, but against the clan
   Of this King I have no charm ;
If they touch water, if they touch wood,
   I cannot work them harm ;
I go a wanderer without rest
Where fingers three touch brow and breast ! "

" God keep thee, Devil," the giant said,
   " Thy riddle I cannot read,
But from thy company here and now
   I must depart with speed ;
I hold thee but as a beaten knave,
To find that mightiest King I crave."

The giant came to an old, old man
   That worked among his bees,
He gathered wax for the altar lights
   In white beneath green trees ;
The sun shone through him, and he, too, shone,
For he was the blessèd Apostle John.

He asked the old man of that king
   Whose bondslave he would be.
"Thro' wood," said St. John, "there is healing in water,
   His servants all are free.''

He christened him and straightway then
Told of the tasks of christened men.

" Some wear the stone with their bent knees,
    Some holy pictures limn,
Some bear the news of Christ to lands
    That have not heard of Him."
The giant said, " If I had the will
For this, I have no wit nor skill."

" To ford," St. John said, " yonder river,
    Poor wayfarers essay,
And by the great swiftness of the stream
    Many are swept away ;
Who carries them over will do a thing
To pleasure greatly the Strong King."

The giant came to that wild water,
    And on its brink did dwell,
He saved the lives of wayfarers
    More than a man may tell ;
And there it chanced one midnight wild
He heard the cry of a little child.

The child held a globe in his hand,
    He begged to cross that night ;
The giant set him on his shoulder
    As a burden sweet and light ;
Into the stream with a careless laugh
He stepped with a palm tree for a staff.

But the child grew heavier and his globe,
    Until they weighed like lead,
" *Deus meus et omnia*,   *My God and all things*
    What child is this ? " he said ;
It seemed as the waves swelled and whirled
He felt the weight of all the world.

Sure, all the churches upon earth
   He bore with tottering feet,
Rouen, Amiens, Bourges, and Chartres,
   Long Sutton, Gedney, Fleet ;
So sweet, so terrible the load,
It was as though he carried God.

The bells of all those churches rang
   When they had gained the shore,
He saw no child, but a great King
   Of might unguessed before ;
The King on whom the world is stayed
That is the Son of the pure Maid.

" I thank thee, Christopher, that thou
   So well hast kept My rule ;
Thou hast borne Me with Heaven My throne
   And the earth My footstool."
He felt strange joy within him stir
As the King called him " Christopher."

On fair days and on market days,
   Where men to fiddles sing,
They tell of the strongest man on earth
   Who served the mightiest King,
For that great King he served so well,
He loves the song and the fiddél.

RICHARD LAWSON GALES.

Once more the poet goes back into the dim ages for his
story, and somehow he manages to make his poem read
a little like an old ballad. Have you felt this, and can
you account for your feeling ?

In which line of the second stanza can be found the
central idea of the story ?

Which stanza, or stanzas, contain the best word-
pictures ?

Who first named the giant ? What does the name
mean ?

Try to make another stanza telling how all wayfarers, especially those who travelled by water, took Christopher for their patron saint (as they actually did).

Faithless Sally Brown

YOUNG Ben he was a nice young man,
    A carpenter by trade ;
And he fell in love with Sally Brown,
    That was a lady's-maid.

But as they fetched a walk one day,
    They met a press-gang crew ;
And Sally she did faint away,
    Whilst Ben he was brought to.

The Boatswain swore with wicked words,
    Enough to shock a saint,
That though she did seem in a fit,
    'Twas nothing but a feint.

" Come, girl," said he, " hold up your head,
    He'll be as good as me ;
For when your swain is in our boat,
    A boat-swain he will be."

So when they'd made their game of her,
    And taken off her elf,
She roused, and found she only was
    A-coming to herself.

" And is he gone, and is he gone ? "
    She cried, and wept outright :
" Then I will to the water side,
    And see him out of sight."

A waterman came up to her,
  " Now, young woman," said he,
" If you weep on so, you will make
  Eye-water in the sea."

" Alas ! they've taken my beau Ben
  To sail with old Benbow ; "
And her woe began to run afresh,
  As if she'd said Gee-woe !

Says he, " They've only taken him
  To the Tender ship, you see ; "
" The Tender ship," cried Sally Brown,
  " What a hard-ship that must be !

" Oh ! would I were a mermaid now,
  For then I'd follow him ;
But oh ! I'm not a fish-woman,
  And so I cannot swim.

" Alas ! I was not born beneath
  The Virgin and the Scales,
So I must curse my cruel stars,
  And walk about in Wales."

Now Ben had sailed to many a place
  That's underneath the world ;
But in two years the ship came home,
  And all her sails were furled.

But when he called on Sally Brown,
  To see how she went on,
He found she'd got another Ben,
  Whose Christian name was John.

" O Sally Brown, O Sally Brown !
  How could you serve me so ?
I've met with many a breeze before,
  But never such a blow."

6

Then reading on his 'bacco box,
    He heaved a bitter sigh,
And then began to eye his pipe,
    And then to pipe his eye.

And then he tried to sing, " All's Well,"
    But could not though he tried :
His head was turned, and so he chewed
    His pigtail till he died.

His death, which happened in his berth,
    At forty-odd befell :
They went and told the sexton, and
    The sexton tolled the bell.

THOMAS HOOD.

Is this a story of the present day ? How can you tell ?

If you do not know, can you tell from the name what a press-gang was ?

John Benbow (1650–1702) was vice-admiral of the British fleet, who spent his whole life in active service at sea. Near Jamaica he attacked a French squadron much greater than his own ; his leg was broken by a shot, but he sat on deck to take charge of the attack. He was defeated owing to lack of support from other officers. He returned to Jamaica, where the officers were punished, and he died of his wounds.

In this poem the writer makes jokes with words which are called puns. Which do you consider the best ? Are there any you do not understand ?

Was Ben a Chinaman ? Why do you think I ask this question ?

What picture, or pictures, would you like to have to illustrate this story ? Compose one of them, making a rough sketch.

Ruth

SHE stood breast-high amid the corn,
Clasped by the golden light of morn ;
Like the sweetheart of the sun,
Who many a glowing kiss had won.

On her cheek an autumn flush
Deeply ripened ; such a blush
In the midst of brown was born,
Like red poppies grown with
    corn.

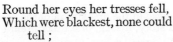

Round her eyes her tresses fell,
Which were blackest, none could
    tell ;
But long lashes veiled a light,
That had else been all too bright.

And her hat, with shady brim,
Made her tressy forehead dim ;
Thus she stood amid the stooks,
Praising God with sweetest looks.

Sure, I said, Heaven did not mean,
Where I reap thou shouldst but glean ;
Lay thy sheaf adown and come,
Share my harvest and my home.

THOMAS HOOD.

Look at the head-dress of the woman in the small picture shown above. It is such a one as Ruth in the Bible story might sometimes wear. Now find a word in the fourth stanza of the poem which shows that this poet is not writing about the original Ruth.

Perhaps the girl in the harvest field really had another name. If so, for what reasons did the poet call her Ruth ? (Do not overlook the second line of the third stanza.)

Who is supposed to be speaking the lines of this poem ?

Find a simile in the first and one in the second stanza.

Study the descriptive words, or epithets—for example, *golden* light ; *glowing* kiss.

Which line of the poem do you like best ? Which line makes the prettiest picture ?

Make a sketch of a stook.

Try to imitate the stanza.   Almost any subject is suitable—for example, the English children in the market-place at Rome :

> They sat forlorn amid the slaves,
> Whose home was far across the waves.

Can you go on ?

What is *personified* in the first stanza of the poem ?
Is this poem a story, a song, or a description ?

The Colubriad

CLOSE by the threshold of a door nailed fast
Three kittens sat ; each kitten looked aghast.
I, passing swift and inattentive by,
At the three kittens cast a careless eye ;
Not much concerned to know what they did there ;
Not deeming kittens worth a poet's care.
But presently a loud and furious hiss
Caused me to stop, and to exclaim, " What's this ? "
When lo ! upon the threshold met my view,
With head erect, and eyes of fiery hue,
A viper, long as Count de Grasse's queue.
Forth from his head his forkèd tongue he throws,
Darting it full against a kitten's nose ;
Who having never seen, in field or house,
The like, sat still and silent as a mouse ;
Only projecting, with attention due,
Her whiskered face, she asked him, " Who are you ? "
On to the hall went I, with pace not slow,
But swift as lightning, for a long Dutch hoe ;
With which well armed I hastened to the spot,
To find the viper, but I found him not.
And turning up the leaves and shrubs around,
Found only that he was not to be found.
But still the kittens, sitting as before,
Sat watching close the bottom of the door.

" I hope," said I, " the villain I would kill
Has slipped between the door and the door-sill ;
And if I make despatch, and follow hard,
No doubt but I shall find him in the yard : "
For long ere now it should have been rehearsed,
'Twas in the garden that I found him first.
E'en there I found him, there the full-grown cat
His head, with velvet paw, did gently pat ;
As curious as the kittens erst had been
To learn what this phenomenon might mean.
Filled with heroic ardour at the sight,
And fearing every moment he would bite,
And rob our household of our only cat
That was of age to combat with a rat,
With outstretched hoe I slew him at the door,
And taught him NEVER TO COME THERE NO MORE.

WILLIAM COWPER.

Note that the title means " the story of the *coluber*,"
the last word being Latin for a harmless snake.

The Count de Grasse was a French admiral who, in
accordance with the fashion of his time, would wear a wig
with a tail.

What effective pictures could be drawn to illustrate
this poem ?

How many stanzas are there in this poem ?

Is it divided into parts in any way ?

Where is the crisis of the story ?   Did you expect the
story to end in this way ?

Does the line used in this poem step along briskly or go
slowly ?   There are five steps, or feet, to each line.   Try
to separate them.

The Nightingale and the Glow-worm

A NIGHTINGALE, that all day long
Had cheered the village with his song,
Nor yet at eve his note suspended,
Nor yet when eventide was ended,

Began to feel, as well he might,
The keen demands of appetite ;
When, looking eagerly around,
He spied, far off, upon the ground,
A something shining in the dark,
And knew the glow-worm by his spark ;
So stooping down from hawthorn top,
He thought to put him in his crop.
The worm, aware of his intent,
Harangued him thus, right eloquent :

" Did you admire my lamp," quoth he,
" As much as I your minstrelsy,
You would abhor to do me wrong,
As much as I to spoil your song ;
For 'twas the self-same Power divine
Taught you to sing and me to shine,
That you with music, I with light,
Might beautify and cheer the night."

The songster heard his short oration,
And, warbling out his approbation,
Released him, as my story tells,
And found a supper somewhere else.
    Hence jarring sectaries may learn
Their real interest to discern ;
That brother should not war with brother,
And worry and devour each other ;
But sing and shine by sweet consent,
Till life's poor transient night is spent ;
Respecting in each other's case
The gifts of nature and of grace.

    Those Christians best deserve the name
Who studiously make peace their aim,
Peace both the duty and the prize
Of him that creeps and him that flies.

WILLIAM COWPER.

Which do you consider the finest lines in this fable ?

Which is the saddest line ?   (Remember that Cowper's persistent ill-health gave him many weary days and still more weary nights.)

Which lines contain the moral of this fable ?

There is a metaphor in the sad line referred to above. What two things are compared ?

Study the length of line and the rhyming in this poem as well as in " The Eagle and the Animals," which follows.

Poets are not always true to fact.   Scientists say that it is the *female* glow-worm which shows the lamp, and the *male* nightingale which sings.

What are " jarring sectaries " ?   Do you like the expression ?   If not, can you suggest a better ?

Would this fable be equally effective in prose ?   Give a full reason for your answer.

Try to put the following story, or at least a portion of it, into verse like the above:

A gay young cock, in the company of two or three hens, was one day raking upon a dunghill, when he happened to scratch up a jewel.   The cock knew what it was well enough, for it sparkled with an exceedingly great brightness ; but not knowing what to do with it, he tried to hide his ignorance under a gay contempt.   So flapping his wings, shaking his head, and putting on an ugly grin, he spoke thus : " Indeed you are a very fine thing, but I do not know what business you have here.   I do not mind telling you that I would rather have one grain of good barley than all the beautiful and brilliant jewels under the sun."

The Eagle and the Animals

As Jupiter's all-seeing eye
Surveyed the worlds beneath the sky,
From this small speck of earth were sent
Murmurs and sounds of discontent ;
For ev'rything alive complained
That he the hardest life sustained.

    Jove calls his Eagle.   At the word
Before him stands the royal bird.

The bird, obedient, from heav'n's height
Downward directs his rapid flight ;
Then cited every living thing
To hear the mandates of his king.

    Ungrateful creatures, whence arise
These murmurs which offend the skies ?
Why this disorder ? say the cause :
For just are Jove's eternal laws.
Let each his discontent reveal ;
To you, sour Dog, I first appeal.

    Hard is my lot, the Hound replies,
On what fleet nerves the Greyhound flies !
While I, with weary step and slow,
O'er plains, and vales, and mountains go ;
The morning sees my chase begun,
Nor ends it till the setting sun.

    When (says the Greyhound) I pursue,
My game is lost, or caught in view ;
Beyond my sight the prey's secure ;
The Hound is slow, but always sure,
And had I his sagacious scent
Jove ne'er had heard my discontent.

    The Lion craved the Fox's art ;
The Fox the Lion's force and heart.
The Cock implored the Pigeon's flight,
Whose wings were rapid, strong, and light ;
The Pigeon strength of wing despised,
And the Cock's matchless valour prized.
The Fishes wished to graze the plain ;
The Beasts to skim beneath the main.
Thus, envious of another's state,
Each blamed the partial hand of Fate.

    The bird of heav'n then cried aloud,
Jove bids disperse the murmuring crowd ;
The god rejects your idle prayers ;
Would ye, rebellious mutineers,
Entirely change your name and nature
And be the very envied creature ?

What ! silent all, and none consent !
Be happy, then, and learn content ;
Nor imitate the restless mind
And proud ambition of mankind.

JOHN GAY.

Why did John Gay, who wrote in a Christian country
(about two hundred years ago), choose to tell of Jupiter ?

The Eagle was Jove's attendant. Can you suggest any
reason why he should choose this particular bird ? What
name is applied to it by the poet ?

What line in this poem suggests the smallness of the
earth in the universe ?

What two lines in the last section of the poem contain
the central idea in Jupiter's solution of the difficulty ?
Which lines form the moral of the fable ?

Try to extend the last section but one. Imagine other
discontented animals speaking—for example,

The Tiger begged the Lion's mane,
The Cat the Dog's bark would attain,

and so on.

There are no quotation marks used in this poem ;
do you miss them ? Is there any place where the omis-
sion of quotation marks makes the meaning just a little
doubtful ?

Baucis and Philemon

IN ancient times, as story tells,
The saints would often leave their cells,
And stroll about, but hide their quality,
To try good people's hospitality.

It happened on a winter night,
As authors of the legend write,
Two brother hermits, saints by trade,
Taking their tour in masquerade,
Disguised in tattered habits went
To a small village down in Kent ;

Where, in the stroller's canting strain,
They begged from door to door in vain,
Tried every tone might pity win ;
But not a soul would take them in.

Our wandering saints, in woeful state,
Treated at this ungodly rate,
Having through all the village passed,
To a small cottage came at last
Where dwelt a good old honest yeoman,
Called in the neighbourhood Philemon ;
Who kindly did these saints invite
In his poor hut to pass the night ;
And then the hospitable sire
Bid goody Baucis mend the fire ;
While he out from the chimney took
A flitch of bacon off the hook,
And freely from the fattest side
Cut out large slices to be fried ;
Then stepped aside to fetch them drink,
Filled a large jug up to the brink,
And saw it fairly twice go round ;
Yet (what is wonderful !) they found
'Twas still replenished to the top,
As if they ne'er had touched a drop.
The good old couple were amazed,
And often on each other gazed ;
For both were frightened to the heart,
And just began to cry, " What art ! "
Then softly turned aside to view
Whether the lights were burning blue.

" Good folks, you need not be afraid,
We are but saints," the hermits said ;
" No hurt shall come to you or yours :
But for that pack of churlish boors,
Not fit to live on Christian ground,
They and their houses shall be drowned ;

Whilst you shall see your cottage rise,
And grow a church before your eyes."

They scarce had spoke, when fair and soft
The roof began to mount aloft,
Aloft rose every beam and rafter,
The heavy wall climbed slowly after ;
The chimney widened and grew higher,
Became a steeple with a spire.

The kettle to the top was hoist,
And there stood fastened to a joist ;
Doomed ever in suspense to dwell,
'Tis now no kettle, but a bell.

A wooden jack which had almost
Lost by disuse the art to roast,
A sudden alteration feels,
Increased by new intestine wheels ;
The jack and chimney, near allied,
Had never left each other's side :
The chimney to a steeple grown,
The jack would not be left alone ;
But up against the steeple reared,
Became a clock, and still adhered.

The groaning chair began to crawl,
Like a huge snail, along the wall ;
There stuck aloft in public view,
And with small change a pulpit grew.

The cottage by such feats as these,
Grown to a church by just degrees,
The hermits then desired the host
To ask for what he fancied most.
Philemon, having paused awhile,
Returned them thanks in homely style :

" I'm old, and fain would live at ease ;
Make me the parson, if you please."

Thus happy in their change of life
Were several years this man and wife.
When on a day, which proved their last,
Discoursing on old stories past,
They went by chance, amidst their talk,
To the churchyard to take a walk ;
When Baucis hastily cried out,
" My dear, I see your forehead sprout ! "
" But yes ! methinks, I feel it true ;
And really yours is budding too—
Nay,—now I cannot stir my foot ;
It feels as if 'twere taking root ! "
Description would but tire my muse ;
In short, they both were turned to yews.

JONATHAN SWIFT.

This story-poem was written by Jonathan (afterwards
Dean) Swift, the author of *Gulliver's Travels*, to please a
little girl named Hester Johnson, whom he called Stella,
and to whom he acted as tutor when he was a young man.
It is a story of ancient Greece, but he altered it and
made it into an English rustic tale, because Stella lived
in the country (at Moor Park, in Middlesex) and would
understand all about flitches of bacon hung on hooks,
and so on.

What do you notice about the length and speed of the
line and about the rhyming ?

The two old people might have cried, " Black Art ! "
If they had, what do you think they would have meant ?

Of whom does the poet make fun near the end of his
verses ?

Can you put in a few more pairs of lines after the last
line but two ?

The Wreck of the Steamship *Puffin*

TELL you a story, children ? Well, gather round my
    knee,
And I'll see if I cannot thrill you (though you're torpid
    after your tea)
With a moving tale of a shipwreck ; and—should you
    refrain from sleep,
For the cake was a trifle heavy—I flatter myself you'll
    weep !

You all know Kensington Gardens, and some of you,
    I'll be bound,
Have stood by the level margin of the Pond that's
    entitled " Round " ;
'Tis a pleasant spot on a summer day, when the air is
    laden with balm,
And the snowy sails are reflected clear in a mirror of
    flawless calm !

Well, it isn't like that in the winter, when the gardens
    are shut at four,
And a wind is lashing the water, and driving the ducks
    ashore.
Ah ! the Pond can be black and cruel then, with its
    waves running inches high,
And a peril lurks for the tautest yacht that pocket-
    money can buy !

Yet, in weather like this, with a howling blast and a
    sky of ominous gloom,
Did the good ship *Puffin* put out to sea, as if trying to
    tempt her doom !

She was a model steamer, on the latest approved
  design,
And her powerful 10-slug engines were driven by
  spirits of wine.

And a smarter crew (they were sixpence each !) never
  shipped on a model bark,
While her Captain, " Nuremberg Noah," had once
  commanded an ark ;
Like a fine old salt of the olden school, he had stuck to
  his wooden ship,
But lately he'd been promoted—and this was his trial
  trip.

Off went the *Puffin* when steam was up, with her
  crew and commander brave !
And her screw was whizzing behind her as she breasted
  the foaming wave ;
Danger ? each sixpenny seaman smiled at the notion
  of that !
But the face of the skipper looked thoughtful from
  under his broad-brimmed hat.

Was he thinking then of his children three—of
  Japheth, and Ham, and Shem ?
Or his elephants (both with a trunk unglued !), was he
  sad at the thought of them ?
Or the door at the end of his own old ark—did it give
  him a passing pain
To reflect that its unreal knocker might never deceive
  him again ?

Nay, children, I cannot answer—he had passed in-
  quiry beyond :
He was far away on the billowy waste of the wild and
  heaving Pond,

Battling hard with the angry crests of the waves, that
    were rolling in
And seeking to overwhelm and swamp his staggering
    vessel of tin !

Suddenly, speed she slackened, and seemed of her task
    to tire . . .
Ay ! for the seas she had shipped of late had extin-
    guished her engine fire !
And the park-keeper, watching her, shook his head
    and in manner unfeeling cried :
" 'Twill be nothing short of a miracle now if she
    makes the opposite side ! "

Think of it, children—that tiny ship, tossed in the
    boiling froth,
Drifting about at the wild caprice of the elements'
    fitful wrath !
Her screw-propeller was useless now that the flickering
    flame was out,
And the invalids gazed from their snug bath-chairs,
    till they almost forgot the gout.

Help for the gallant vessel ! she is overborne by the
    blast !
She is shipping water by spoonfuls now, I tell you,
    she's sinking fast !
" Hi ! " cried one of her owners to a spaniel, liver and
    black,
"Good dog, into the water, quick ! " . . . But the park-
    keeper held it back !

Yes, spite of indignant pleadings from the eager,
    excited crowd,
He quoted a pedant by-law : " In the water no dogs
    allowed."

Then shame on the regulations that would hinder an
   honest dog
From plunging in to assist a ship that is rolling a help-
   less log !

Stand by all ! for she'll ride it out—though she's left
   to do it alone.
She was drifting in, she was close at hand—when down
   she went like a stone !
A few feet more and they had her safe—and now, it
   was all too late,
For the *Puffin* had foundered in sight of port, by
   a stroke of ironical Fate !

But the other owner was standing by, and, tossing her
   tangled locks,
Down she sat on the nearest seat—and took off her
   shoes and socks !
" One kiss, brother ! " she murmured, " one clutch of
   your strong right hand—
And *I'll* paddle out to the *Puffin* and bring her in
   safe to land ! "

What can a barefooted child do ?   More than the pam-
   pered cur,
With his chicken-fed carcass shrinking, afraid from
   the bank to stir !
More than a baffled spaniel—ay, and more than the
   pug-dog pet,
That wrinkles his ebony muzzle, and whines if his
   paws are wet !

" Come back ! " the park-keeper shouted—but she
   merely answered, " I *won't* ! "
And into the water she waded—though the invalids
   whimpered " Don't ! "

Ah ! but the Pond struck chilly, and the mud at the
  bottom was thick ;
But in she paddled, and probed it with the point of a
  borrowed stick !

" Don't let go of me, darling ! " " Keep hold of my
  fingers tight,
And I'll have it out in a minute or two. . . . I haven't
  got up to it quite :
A minute more, and the sunken ship we'll safe to the
  surface bring,
Yes, and the sixpenny sailors, too, that we lashed to
  the funnel with string ! "

Up to the knees in the water, Ethel and brother Ralph
Groped till they *found* the *Puffin* and her sailors—
  soppy, but *safe !*
All the dear little sailors ! . . . but, children, I can't go on !
For poor old wooden-faced Noah—*how* shall I tell
  you ?—gone !

He must have fallen over, out of that heeling boat,
Away in the dim grey offing, to rise and to fall like a
  float,
Till the colour deserted his face and form, as it might
  at an infant's suck,
And he sank to his rest in his sailor's tomb—the maw
  of a hungry duck !

You are weeping ? I cannot wonder. Mine is a
  pathetic style.
Weep for him, children, freely . . . but, when you have
  finished, smile
With joy for his shipmates, rescued as though by a
  Prospero's wand,
And the *Puffin* snatched from the slimy depths of the
  Round but treacherous Pond !

F. ANSTEY.

7

The opening of this poem leads us to expect a story of heroism. Well, we get it, in a way, but it is a kind of mock-heroism ; so the poem is said to be written in the " mock-heroic " style. Try to tell a history story, say the story of Henry Hudson, who was cast away in a boat by mutineers, in the true heroic style, using the same form of verse—for example :

> Tell you a story, children ? Well, gather around
>   my knee,
> And I'll see if I cannot thrill you with a tale of a
>   frozen [or the Northern] sea—
> A moving tale of a mutiny, and should . . .

Can you go on ?

Borrow from the library a book by Sir J. M. Barrie called *Peter Pan in Kensington Gardens*, which will tell you all about the Round Pond and about Peter.

What is the *metaphor* in the third line of the second stanza ? Are there any other metaphors in the poem ?

Why *Nuremberg* Noah ? (The poem was written before the war interfered, for a time only, with the kindly feeling between the woodcutters of South Germany and the children of English homes. Nuremberg was, and is, the kind of old town that any of Hans Andersen's stories or Grimm's Tales might have sprung from.)

A sketch would be useful to go with the sixth stanza and another for the seventh, which must be read with thoughtfulness and a kind of serious solemnity.

You may need a dictionary for *torpid*, and *pedant*, and *ironical*, and a few more words, but not while the tragedy is being unfolded.

What picture would you like a good artist to paint for this poem ?

Study the rhymes and find out how the writer pronounced *Ralph*.

You can find out all about Prospero and his wand from *The Tempest* in Lamb's *Tales from Shakespeare*.

Feigned Courage

HORATIO of ideal courage vain,
Was flourishing in air his father's cane,
And, as the fumes of valour swelled his pate,
Now thought himself *this* hero, and now *that* :
" And now," he cried, " I will Achilles be ;
My sword I brandish ; see, the Trojans flee !
Now I'll be Hector, when his angry blade
A lane though heaps of slaughtered Grecians made !
And now by deeds still braver, I'll evince
I am no less than Edward the Black Prince.—
Give way, ye coward French ! "—As thus he spoke,
And aimed in fancy a sufficient stroke
To fix the fate of Cressy or Poictiers
(The Muse relates the hero's fate with tears),
He struck his milk-white hand against a nail,
Sees his own blood and feels his courage fail.
Ah ! where is now that boasted valour flown
That in the tented field so late was shown ?
Achilles weeps, great Hector hangs his head,
And the Black Prince goes whimpering to bed.

From *Poetry for Children*, by
CHARLES and MARY LAMB.

You may, after studying the rhymes and the structure
of these lines, find it possible to continue Horatio's boast-
ing about the heroes ; for example :

" And now," he said, " I am King Harry Five ;
No Frenchman in my sight remains alive ;
Now I'll be Wellington . . ."

What is there peculiar about the eighth line ?
Study the length of line, feet, and rhymes of this poem.
Can you find any reason for saying that the poem is
" mock-heroic " ?

The Singing Leaves

I

" WHAT fairings will ye that I bring ? "
　Said the king to his daughters three ;
" For I to Vanity Fair am bound,
　Now say what shall they be ? "

Then up and spake the eldest daughter,
　That lady tall and grand :
" Oh, bring me pearls and diamonds great,
　And gold rings for my hand."

Thereafter spake the second daughter,
　That was both white and red :
" For me bring silks that will stand alone,
　And a gold comb for my head."

Then came the turn of the least daughter,
　That was whiter than thistledown,
And among the gold of her blithesome hair
　Dim shone the golden crown.

" There came a bird this morning
　And sang 'neath my bower eaves,
Till I dreamed, as his music made me,
　' Ask thou for the Singing Leaves.' "

Then the brow of the king swelled crimson
　With a flush of angry scorn :
" Well have ye spoken, my two eldest,
　And chosen as ye were born ;

" But she, like a thing of peasant race,
　That is happy binding the sheaves ; "
Then he saw her dead mother in her face,
　And said, " Thou shalt have thy leaves."

II

He mounted and rode three days and nights
   Till he came to Vanity Fair,
And 'twas easy to buy the gems and the silk,
   But no Singing Leaves were there.

Then deep in the greenwood rode he,
   And asked of every tree,
" Oh, if you have ever a Singing Leaf,
   I pray you give it me ! "

But the trees all kept their counsel,
   And never a word said they,
Only there sighed from the pine-tops
   A music of seas far away.

Only the pattering aspen
   Made a sound of growing rain,
That fell ever faster and faster,
   Then faltered to silence again.

" Oh, where shall I find a little foot-page
   That would win both hose and shoon,
And will bring to me the Singing Leaves
   If they grow under the moon ? "

Then lightly turned him Walter the page,
   By the stirrup as he ran :
" Now pledge you me the truesome word
   Of a king and gentleman,

" That you will give me the first, first thing
   You meet at your castle gate,
And the Princess shall get the Singing Leaves,
   Or mine be a traitor's fate."

The king's head dropped upon his breast
    A moment, as it might be ;
'Twill be my dog, he thought, and said,
    " My faith I plight to thee."

Then Walter took from next his heart
    A packet small and thin :
" Now give you this to the Princess Anne,
    The Singing Leaves are therein."

III

As the king rode in at his castle gate
    A maiden to meet him ran,
And " Welcome, father ! " she laughed and cried
    Together, the Princess Anne.

" Lo, here the Singing Leaves," quoth he,
    " And woe, but they cost me dear ! "
She took the packet, and the smile
    Deepened down beneath the tear.

It deepened down till it reached her heart,
    And then gushed up again,
And lighted her eyes as the sudden sun
    Transfigures the summer rain.

And the first Leaf, when it was opened,
    Sang : " I am Walter the page,
And the songs I sing 'neath thy window
    Are my only heritage."

And the second Leaf sang : " But in the land
    That is neither on earth nor sea,
My lute and I are lords of more
    Than thrice this kingdom's fee."

And the third Leaf sang, " Be mine ! be mine ! "
   And ever it sang, " Be mine ! "
Then sweeter it sang and ever sweeter,
   And said, " I am thine, thine, thine ! "

At the first Leaf she grew pale enough,
   At the second she turned aside,
At the third, 'twas as if a lily flushed
   With a rose's red heart's tide.

" Good counsel gave the bird," said she,
   " I have my hope thrice o'er,
For they sing to my very heart," she said,
   " And it sings to them evermore."

She brought to him her beauty and truth,
   But and broad earldoms three,
And he made her queen of the broader lands
   He held of his lute in fee.
               J. RUSSELL LOWELL.

Re-read the poem (another imitation of an old ballad)
as a kind of play, taking parts, while a *Lector* quietly
reads the parts which are not spoken.   Like this :

King. What fairings will ye that I bring ?
Lector. Said the king to his daughters three.
King. For I to Vanity Fair am bound,
    Now say what shall they be ?
Lector. Then up and spake the eldest daughter,
    That lady tall and grand.
Eldest D. Oh, bring me pearls and diamonds great,
    And gold rings for my hand——

and so on throughout.
   Select the phrases which describe the appearance of
each of the three daughters.   How could a girl's hair be
called *blithesome,* which means glad or merry ?
   What kind of wealth has one who can make sweet
music ?

What picture would you like to have to go with this story ?   How would you compose it ?

Find out from the way the story goes the meaning of the following phrases : kept their counsel ; hose and shoon ; a traitor's fate ; my faith I plight ; they cost me dear ; transfigures the summer rain ; my only heritage ; thrice the kingdom's fee ; queen of the broader lands.

It is not *very* hard to write a story in this verse form. Select a short fairy tale and tell it in the ballad stanza.

The Sleeping Beauty

THE SLEEP

I

YEAR after year unto her feet,
    She lying on her couch alone,
Across the purpled coverlet,
    The maiden's jet-black hair has grown,
On either side her trancèd form
    Forth streaming from a braid of pearl :
The slumbrous light is rich and warm,
    And moves not on the rounded curl.

II

The silk star-broidered coverlid
    Unto her limbs itself doth mould
Languidly ever ; and, amid
    Her full black ringlets downward rolled,
Glows forth each softly-shadowed arm
    With bracelets of the diamond bright :
Her constant beauty doth inform
    Stillness with love, and day with light.

III

She sleeps : her breathings are not heard
    In palace chambers far apart.
The fragrant tresses are not stirred
    That lie upon her charmèd heart.
She sleeps : on either hand upswells
    The gold-fringed pillow lightly prest :
She sleeps, nor dreams, but ever dwells
    A perfect form in perfect rest.

THE ARRIVAL

I

All precious things, discovered late,
    To those that seek them issue forth ;
For love in sequel works with fate,
    And draws the veil from hidden worth.
He travels far from other skies—
    His mantle glitters on the rocks—
A fairy Prince, with joyful eyes,
    And lighter-footed than the fox.

II

The bodies and the bones of those
    That strove in other days to pass,
Are withered in the thorny close,
    Or scattered blanching on the grass.
He gazes on the silent dead :
    " They perished in their daring deeds."
This proverb flashes through his head,
    " The many fail ; the one succeeds."

III

He comes, scarce knowing what he seeks :
    He breaks the hedge : he enters there :

The colour flies into his cheeks :
    He trusts to light on something fair ;
For all his life the charm did talk
    About his path, and hover near
With words of promise in his walk,
    And whispered voices at his ear.

IV

More close and close his footsteps wind :
    The Magic Music in his heart
Beats quick and quicker, till he find
    The quiet chamber far apart.
His spirit flutters like a lark,
    He stoops—to kiss her—on his knee.
" Love, if thy tresses be so dark,
    How dark those hidden eyes must be ! "

THE REVIVAL

I

A touch, a kiss ! the charm was snapt.
    There rose a noise of striking clocks,
And feet that ran, and doors that clapt,
    And barking dogs, and crowing cocks ;
A fuller light illumined all,
    A breeze through all the garden swept,
A sudden hubbub shook the hall,
    And sixty feet the fountain leapt.

II

The hedge broke in, the banner blew,
    The butler drank, the steward scrawled,
The fire shot up, the martin flew,
    The parrot screamed, the peacock squalled,

The maid and page renewed their strife,
   The palace banged, and buzzed and clackt,
And all the long-pent stream of life
   Dashed downward in a cataract.

III

And last with these the king awoke,
   And in his chair himself upreared,
And yawned, and rubbed his face, and spoke,
   " By holy rood, a royal beard !
How say you ? we have slept, my lords.
   My beard has grown into my lap."
The barons swore, with many words,
   'Twas but an after-dinner's nap.

IV

" Pardy," returned the king, " but still
   My joints are something stiff or so.
My lord, and shall we pass the bill
   I mentioned half an hour ago ? "
The chancellor, sedate and vain,
   In courteous words returned reply :
But dallied with his golden chain,
   And, smiling, put the question by.

THE DEPARTURE

I

And on her lover's arm she leant,
   And round her waist she felt it fold,
And far across the hills they went
   In that new world which is the old :
Across the hills and far away
   Beyond their utmost purple rim,
And deep into the dying day
   The happy princess followed him.

II

" I'd sleep another hundred years,
　　O love, for such another kiss ; "
" O wake for ever, love," she hears,
　　" O love, 'twas such as this and this."
And o'er them many a sliding star,
　　And many a merry wind was borne,
And, streamed through many a golden bar,
　　The twilight melted into morn.

III

" O eyes long laid in happy sleep ! "
　　" O happy sleep, that lightly fled ! "
" O happy kiss, that woke thy sleep ! "
　　" O love, thy kiss would wake the dead ! "
And o'er them many a flowing range
　　Of vapour buoyed the crescent-bark,
And, rapt through many a rosy change,
　　The twilight died into the dark.

IV

" A hundred summers ! can it be
　　And whither goest thou, tell me where ? "
" O seek my father's court with me,
　　For there are greater wonders there."
And o'er the hills, and far away
　　Beyond their utmost purple rim,
Beyond the night, across the day,
　　Through all the world she followed him.

LORD TENNYSON.

This is, of course, the old tale of Briar Rose put into
verse form.　The poet took great pains with the story.
There are no rough or halting lines, as in the old ballads ;
the stresses or accents fall regularly (four feet to a line) ;
and the rhymes are nearly all as sound as a bell.

Does he tell the story seriously or lightly, making a little fun of it?

Can you find something like the old ballads in the first stanza of " The Arrival "?

Which lines sound best to your ear and are most easily remembered?

Try to write a stanza of your own on some other fairy tale.

The East Wind and the Morning Star

[The Indians of North America say that in the olden days the East Wind was given to Wabun.]

YOUNG and beautiful was Wabun ;
He it was who brought the morning,
He it was whose silver arrows
Chased the dark o'er hill and valley ;
He it was whose cheeks were painted
With the brightest streaks of crimson,
And whose voice awoke the village,
Called the deer and called the hunter.

Lonely in the sky was Wabun ;
Though the birds sang gaily to him,
Though the wild-flowers of the meadow
Filled the air with odours for him,
Though the forests and the rivers
Sang and shouted at his coming,
Still his heart was sad within him,
For he was alone in heaven.

But one morning, gazing earthward
While the village still was sleeping,
And the fog lay on the river,
Like a ghost, that goes at sunrise,
He beheld a maiden walking
All alone upon a meadow,

Gathering water-flags and rushes
By a river in the meadow.

Every morning, gazing earthward,
Still the first thing he beheld there
Was her blue eyes looking at him,
Two blue lakes among the rushes.
And he loved the lonely maiden,
Who thus waited for his coming ;
For they both were solitary,
She on earth and he in heaven.

And he wooed her with caresses,
Wooed her with his smile of sunshine,
With his flattering words he wooed her,
With his sighing and his singing,
Gentlest whispers in the branches,
Softest music, sweetest odours,
Till he drew her to his bosom,
Folded in his robes of crimson,
Till into a star he changed her,
Trembling still upon his bosom ;
And for ever in the heavens
They were seen together walking,
Wabun and the Wabun-Annung,
Wabun and the Star of Morning.

H. W. LONGFELLOW.

The poet who made up this story had often watched
the day break. He had felt the gentle eastern breeze
that so often rises to blow away the darkness, and just
before the sun rose, while the eastern sky was beginning
to brighten, he had seen the morning star twinkling in
the heavens. So to him the East Wind became a young
man who was very strong but also very gentle, and the
Morning Star a blue-eyed lovely girl. And they were
married, and lived happy ever after.

Describe the young man Wabun from the details given
in the first stanza. One line in the last stanza tells you
something about his robe.

Read the second stanza again very carefully, to find out what happens at the dawn. Can you think of anything that the poet has not mentioned ? (There is something more mentioned in the third stanza.)

What does the poet mean by " two blue lakes " ?

This reading is from the long poem called *The Song of Hiawatha*, written by H. W. Longfellow. You must read the whole of it some day to find out all about the adventures of the great and good Red Indian chief.

Make a drawing of a water-flag, and another of a clump of bulrushes.

Lochinvar

OH, young Lochinvar is come out of the west,
Through all the wide Border his steed was the best ;
And save his good broadsword he weapon had none,
He rode all unarmed, and he rode all alone.
So faithful in love, and so dauntless in war,
There never was knight like the young Lochinvar.

He stayed not for brake, and he stopped not for stone,
He swam the Esk river where ford there was none ;
But ere he alighted at Netherby gate,
The bride had consented, the gallant came late ;
For a laggard in love, and a dastard in war,
Was to wed the fair Ellen of brave Lochinvar.

So boldly he entered the Netherby Hall,
Among bride's-men and kinsmen and brothers and all :
Then spoke the bride's father, his hand on his sword,
(For the poor craven bridegroom said never a word,)
" Oh, come ye in peace here, or come ye in war,
Or to dance at our bridal, young Lord Lochinvar ? "

" I long wooed your daughter, my suit you denied ;—
Love swells like the Solway, but ebbs like its tide—

And now am I come, with this lost love of mine,
To lead but one measure, drink one cup of wine.
There are maidens in Scotland more lovely by far,
That would gladly be bride to the young Lochinvar."

The bride kissed the goblet, the knight took it up,
He quaffed off the wine, and he threw down the cup.
She looked down to blush and she looked up to
sigh,
With a smile on her lips and a tear in her eye.
He took her soft hand, ere her mother could bar—
" Now tread we a measure," said young Lochinvar.

So stately his form, and so lovely her face,
That never a hall such a galliard did grace ;
While her mother did fret, and her father did fume,
And the bridegroom stood dangling his bonnet and
plume ;
And the bride-maidens whispered, " 'Twere better by
far
To have matched our fair cousin with young Loch-
invar."

One touch to her hand, and one word in her ear,
When they reached the hall-door and the charger
stood near,
So light to the croupe the fair lady he swung,
So light to the saddle before her he sprung !
" She is won ! We are gone, over bank, bush, and
scaur ;
They'll have fleet steeds that follow," quoth young
Lochinvar.

There was mounting 'mong Graemes of the Netherby
clan ;
Forsters, Fenwicks, and Musgraves, they rode and
they ran ;

There was racing, and chasing, on Cannobie Lee,
But the lost bride of Netherby ne'er did they see.
So daring in love, and so dauntless in war,
Have you e'er heard of gallant like young Lochinvar?

SIR WALTER SCOTT.

Read one or two stanzas of this poem aloud. Of what does the sound remind you?

Find the Border country on a map showing Great Britain.

Was Lochinvar a Scot or an Englishman?

Is the fourth line of the first verse quite true?

What is meant by "laggard in love" and "dastard in war"? What else is the bridegroom called in a later line of the poem?

How could you tell from certain words in the third stanza that Netherby was on the English side of the Border?

Does the first line in the fourth verse mean that the father objected to Lochinvar's *dress*?

Note that the tide comes in and goes out very quickly over the flats of the Solway. Where is the Solway Firth?

What do you think of the last two lines of the fourth stanza?

Note that a galliard was a French dance.

Was the croupe before or behind the saddle?

Who is the chief figure in the story? Who come next in importance? Who are in the background of the tale?

Study the rhyming of the lines.

How many heavier syllables are there in each line?

Try to write a verse telling how Lochinvar brought his stolen bride home.

How would the bride's mother tell this story to her ladies?

The Inchcape Rock

No stir in the air, no stir in the sea,
The ship was still as she could be,
Her sails from heaven received no motion,
Her keel was steady in the ocean.

(2,873)

8

Without either sign or sound of their shock
The waves flowed over the Inchcape Rock;
So little they rose, so little they fell,
They did not move the Inchcape Bell.

The Abbot of Aberbrothok
Had placed that bell on the Inchcape Rock;
On a buoy in the storm it floated and swung,
And óver the waves its warning rung.

When the Rock was hid by the surge's swell,
The mariners heard the warning bell;
And then they knew the perilous Rock,
And blest the Abbot of Aberbrothok.

The Sun in heaven was shining gay,
All things were joyful on that day;
The sea-birds screamed as they wheeled round,
And there was joyaunce in their sound.

The buoy of the Inchcape Bell was seen
A darker speck on the ocean green;
Sir Ralph the Rover walked his deck,
And he fixed his eye on the darker speck.

He felt the cheering power of spring,
It made him whistle, it made him sing;
His heart was mirthful to excess,
But the Rover's mirth was wickedness.

His eye was on the Inchcape float;
Quoth he, " My men, put out the boat,
And row me to the Inchcape Rock,
And I'll plague the Abbot of Aberbrothok."

The boat is lowered, the boatmen row,
And to the Inchcape Rock they go;
Sir Ralph bent over from the boat,
And he cut the Bell from the Inchcape float.

Down sunk the Bell with a gurgling sound,
The bubbles rose and burst around ;
Quoth Sir Ralph, " The next who comes to the Rock
Won't bless the Abbot of Aberbrothok."

Sir Ralph the Rover sailed away,
He scoured the seas for many a day ;
And now grown rich with plundered store,
He steers his course for Scotland's shore.

So thick a haze o'erspreads the sky,
They cannot see the Sun on high ;
The wind hath blown a gale all day,
At evening it hath died away.

On deck the Rover takes his stand,
So dark it is they see no land.
Quoth Sir Ralph, " It will be lighter soon,
For there is the dawn of the rising Moon."

" Canst hear," said one, " the breakers roar ?
For methinks we should be near the shore."
" Now where we are I cannot tell,
But I wish I could hear the Inchcape Bell."

They hear no sound, the swell is strong ;
Though the wind hath fallen they drift along,
Till the vessel strikes with a shivering shock,—
" O Christ ! it is the Inchcape Rock ! "

Sir Ralph the Rover tore his hair ;
He cursed himself in his despair ;
The waves rushed in on every side,
The ship is sinking beneath the tide.

But even in his dying fear
One dreadful sound could the Rover hear,
A sound as if with the Inchcape Bell,
The Devil below was ringing his knell.

ROBERT SOUTHEY.

Study the first stanza very carefully. Another poet, who knew Southey well, put the same idea of stillness on the sea into the following lines :

> " Day after day, day after day,
>   We stuck, nor breath nor motion ;
>   As idle as a painted ship
>   Upon a painted ocean."

Which stanza do you prefer ?

Has Southey made his poem, in any way—subject or form—like an old ballad ?

Why did Sir Ralph " cut the Bell from the Inchcape Rock " ?

Are there any lines which give the sense by the sound ? (Read the poem aloud.)

In which other poems of this book does a wicked person get his (or her) deserts ?

Lord Ullin's Daughter

A CHIEFTAIN to the Highlands bound
    Cries, " Boatman, do not tarry !
And I'll give thee a silver pound
    To row us o'er the ferry ! "

" Now who be ye would cross Lochgyle,
    This dark and stormy water ? "
" Oh, I'm the chief of Ulva's isle,
    And this, Lord Ullin's daughter.

" And fast before her father's men
    Three days we've fled together ;
For should he find us in the glen,
    My blood would stain the heather.

" His horsemen hard behind us ride—
    Should they our steps discover,
Then who will cheer my bonnie bride,
    When they have slain her lover ? "

Out spoke the hardy Highland wight,
  " I'll go, my chief, I'm ready :
It is not for your silver bright,
  But for your winsome lady :

" And by my word ! the bonnie bird
  In danger shall not tarry ;
So though the waves are raging white
  I'll row you o'er the ferry."

By this the storm grew loud apace,
  The water-wraith was shrieking ;
And in the scowl of heaven each face
  Grew dark as they were speaking.

But still as wilder blew the wind,
  And as the night grew drearer,
Adown the glen rode armèd men,
  Their trampling sounded nearer.

" Oh haste thee, haste ! " the lady cries,
  " Though tempests round us gather ;
I'll meet the raging of the skies,
  But not an angry father."

The boat has left a stormy land,
  A stormy sea before her,—
When, oh ! too strong for human hand,
  The tempest gathered o'er her.

And still they rowed amidst the roar
  Of waters fast prevailing :
Lord Ullin reached that fatal shore,—
  His wrath was changed to wailing.

For, sore dismayed, through storm and shade,
  His child he did discover ;—
One lovely hand she stretched for aid,
  And one was round her lover.

" Come back ! come back ! " he cried in grief,
   " Across this stormy water ;
And I'll forgive your Highland chief,
   My daughter !   O my daughter ! "

'Twas vain : the loud waves lashed the shore,
   Return or aid preventing :
The waters wild went o'er his child,
   And he was left lamenting.

T. CAMPBELL.

This is a ballad poem, old in subject and in form, but written by a poet who lived between 1777 and 1844.

It ought to be read aloud, for it is a good " sound poem."   Note especially the seventh and eighth stanzas.

If you were an artist, which parts of the story would you choose to illustrate ?

Jock of Hazeldean

" WHY weep ye by the tide, ladie ?
   Why weep ye by the tide ?
I'll wed ye to my youngest son,
   And ye sall be his bride :
And ye sall be his bride, ladie,
   Sae comely to be seen "—
But aye she loot the tears down fa'
   For Jock of Hazeldean.

" Now let this wilfu' grief be done,
   And dry that cheek so pale ;
Young Frank is chief of Errington
   And lord of Langley-dale ;
His step is first in peaceful ha',
   His sword in battle keen "—
But aye she loot the tears down fa'
   For Jock of Hazeldean.

" A chain of gold ye sall not lack,
　　Nor braid to bind your hair,
Nor mettled hound, nor managed hawk,
　　Nor palfrey fresh and fair ;
And you the foremost o' them a'
　　Sall ride our forest-queen "—
But aye she loot the tears down fa'
　　For Jock of Hazeldean.

The kirk was decked at morning-tide,
　　The tapers glimmered fair ;
The priest and bridegroom wait the bride,
　　And dame and knight are there :
They sought her baith by bower and ha' ;
　　The ladie was not seen !—
She's o'er the Border, and awa'
　　Wi' Jock of Hazeldean.

SIR WALTER SCOTT.

Of which other poem in this book does this song remind you ?

Who is speaking in the first three stanzas ? Where did Scott probably get the idea of beginning the story without any explanations ?

What is the refrain of the poem ? Find a similar device in an old ballad.

Why did the lovers fly over the Border.

Imagine that they met young Lochinvar and his stolen bride, and write a stanza to tell what happened —if you can.

The Soldier's Dream

OUR bugles sang truce, for the night-cloud had lowered,
　　And the sentinel stars set their watch in the sky ;
And thousands had sunk on the ground overpowered
　　The weary to sleep, and the wounded to die.

When reposing that night on my pallet of straw
　　By the wolf-scaring fagot that guarded the slain,
At the dead of the night a sweet Vision I saw,
　　And thrice ere the morning I dreamt it again.

Methought from the battlefield's dreadful array
　　Far, far I had roamed on a desolate track :
'Twas Autumn, and sunshine arose on the way
　　To the home of my fathers, that welcomed me back.

I flew to the pleasant fields traversed so oft
　　In life's morning march, when my bosom was young ;
I heard my own mountain-goats bleating aloft,
　　And knew the sweet strain that the corn-reapers
　　　　sung.

Then pledged we the wine-cup, and fondly I swore
　　From my home and my weeping friends never to
　　　　part ;
My little ones kissed me a thousand times o'er,
　　And my wife sobbed aloud in her fullness of heart.

" Stay—stay with us !—rest !—thou art weary and
　　　　worn ! "—
　　And fain was their war-broken soldier to stay ;—
But sorrow returned with the dawning of morn,
　　And the voice in my dreaming ear melted away.

T. CAMPBELL.

Is this a story-poem or a poem of incident ?   Does the
poet name any particular war or any particular soldier ?
Was he a British soldier ?
　Which lines make you feel most deeply ?
　But—does the poet make the speaker talk like a real
soldier ?

After Blenheim

IT was a summer evening,
  Old Kaspar's work was done,
And he before his cottage door
  Was sitting in the sun,
And by him sported on the green
His little grandchild Wilhelmine.

She saw her brother Peterkin,
  Roll something large and round,
Which he beside the rivulet
  In playing there had found ;
He came to ask what he had found
That was so large and smooth and round.

Old Kaspar took it from the boy,
  Who stood expectant by ;
And then the old man shook his head,
  And with a natural sigh—
" 'Tis some poor fellow's skull," said he,
" Who fell in the great victory.

" I find them in the garden,
  For there's many here about ;
And often when I go to plough
  The ploughshare turns them out !
For many thousand men," said he,
" Were slain in that great victory."

" Now tell us what 'twas all about,"
  Young Peterkin he cries :
And little Wilhelmine looks up
  With wonder-waiting eyes ;
" Now tell us all about the war,
And what they fought each other for."

" It was the English," Kaspar cried,
  " Who put the French to rout ;
But what they fought each other for
  I could not well make out.
But everybody said," quoth he,
" That 'twas a famous victory.

" My father lived at Blenheim then,
  Yon little stream hard by ;
They burnt his dwelling to the ground,
  And he was forced to fly ;
So with his wife and child he fled,
Nor had he where to rest his head.

" With fire and sword the country round
  Was wasted far and wide,
And many a childing mother then
  And new-born baby died ;
But things like that, you know, must be
At every famous victory.

" They say it was a shocking sight,
  After the field was won ;
For many thousand bodies here
  Lay rotting in the sun ;
But things like that, you know, must be
After a famous victory.

" Great praise the Duke of Marlbro' won,
  And our good Prince Eugene."
" Why, 'twas a very wicked thing ! "
  Said little Wilhelmine.
" Nay, nay, my little girl," quoth he,
" It was a famous victory.

" And everybody praised the Duke
  Who this great fight did win."

" But what good came of it at last ? "
   Quoth little Peterkin.
" Why, that I cannot tell," said he,
" But 'twas a famous victory."

ROBERT SOUTHEY.

What is the refrain of this poem ?
Do you think the poet liked war and bloodshed ?
Look up your history book. What *was* it that " they fought each other for " ?
This new kind of stanza is interesting in shape and rhymes. The first stanza makes a pretty contrast with the warlike subject of the poem. Try to imitate it, describing an indoor scene in winter—say at Christmas time.

Incident

CHARACTERISTIC OF A FAVOURITE DOG

[This dog I knew well. It belonged to Mrs. Wordsworth's brother, Mr. Thomas Hutchinson, who then lived at Stockton on the Tees, a beautiful retired situation, where I used to visit him and his sisters before my marriage. My sister and I spent many months there after our return from Germany in 1799.—WORDSWORTH.]

ON his morning rounds the Master
Goes to learn how all things fare ;
Searches pasture after pasture,
Sheep and cattle eyes with care ;
And, for silence or for talk,
He hath comrades in his walk ;
Four dogs, each pair of different breed,
Distinguished two for scent, and two for speed.

See a hare before him started !
—Off they fly in earnest chase ;
Every dog is eager-hearted,
All the four are in the race :

And the hare whom they pursue,
Knows from instinct what to do ;
Her hope is near : no turn she makes ;
But, like an arrow, to the river takes.

Deep the river was, and crusted
Thinly by a one night's frost ;
But the nimble hare hath trusted
To the ice, and safely crost ;
She hath crost, and without heed
All are following at full speed,
When, lo ! the ice, so thinly spread,
Breaks—and the greyhound, DART, is over-head !

Better fate have PRINCE and SWALLOW—
See them cleaving to the sport !
MUSIC has no heart to follow,
Little MUSIC, she stops short.
She hath neither wish nor heart,
Hers is now another part :
A loving creature she, and brave !
And fondly strives her struggling friend to save.

From the brink her paws she stretches,
Very hands as you would say !
And afflicting moans she fetches,
As he breaks the ice away.
For herself she hath no fears,—
Him alone she sees and hears,—
Makes efforts with complainings ; nor gives o'er
Until her fellow sinks to reappear no more.

W. WORDSWORTH.

Is this poem one of slow or quick action ? Does the
length of line and the arrangement of syllables suit it ?
Would it make a good film ?
How could you make the story end happily ?
How does the sound show the sense in " Little Music,
she stops short " ?

What is the meaning of the poem's rather strange title?

It is not easy to imitate this kind of stanza. Study the rhymes and say which ring soundest. Then try to tell the following story in verse:

Our little robin has visited us several winters now. He hops on to the window-sill, puffs himself out, and regards us very knowingly as we put out his crumbs.

One day, on entering one of the bedrooms, we found our little friend perched on the dressing-table and gazing fixedly at his reflection in the mirror. We watched him for several minutes. He looked very puzzled, and tapped the mirror with his beak several times, and finally flew out of the window, but returned soon afterwards with a nice plump worm in his beak. He laid it down in front of the mirror, waited a moment, and then flew out again.

He evidently took his reflection for another robin, which he hoped to entice out of doors with a worm.

Echo and the Ferry

Ay, Oliver! I was but seven, and he was eleven;
He looked at me pouting and rosy. I blushed where
    I stood.
They had told us to play in the orchard (and I only
    seven!
A small guest at the farm); but he said, " Oh, a girl
    was no good,"
So he whistled and went, he went over the stile to the
    wood.
It was sad, it was sorrowful! Only a girl—only seven!
At home in the dark London smoke I had not found
    it out.
The pear-trees looked on in their white, and blue
    birds flashed about;
And they, too, were angry as Oliver. Were they
    eleven!
I thought so. Yes, every one else was eleven—
    eleven!

So Oliver went, but the cowslips were tall at my feet,
And all the white orchard with fast-falling blossom
    was littered,
And under and over the branches those little birds
    twittered,
While, hanging head downwards, they scolded because
    I was seven.
A pity. A very great pity. One should be eleven.
But soon I was happy, the smell of the world was so
    sweet,
And I saw a round hole in an apple-tree rosy and old.
Then I knew ! for I peeped, and I felt it was right they
    should scold !
Eggs small and eggs many. For gladness I broke into
    laughter ;
And then some one else—oh, how softly ! came after,
    came after
With laughter—with laughter came after.

And no one was near us to utter that sweet mocking
    call,
That soon very tired sank low with a mystical fall.
But this was the country—perhaps it was close under
    heaven ;
Oh, nothing so likely ; the voice might have come
    from it even.
I knew about heaven. But this was the country, of
    this
Light, blossom, and piping, and flashing of wings not
    at all.
Not at all. No. But one little bird was an easy
    forgiver :
She peeped, she drew near as I moved from her
    domicile small,
Then flashed down her hole like a dart—like a dart
    from a quiver.
And I waded atween the long grasses and felt it was
    bliss.

So this was the country ; clear dazzle of azure and
   shiver
And whisper of leaves, and a humming all over the tall
White branches, a humming of bees. And I came to
   the wall—
A little low wall—and looked over, and there was the
   river,
The lane that led on to the village, and then the sweet
   river,
Clear-shining and slow, she had far, far to go from her
   snow ;
But each rush gleamed a sword in the sunlight to
   guard her long flow,
And she murmured methought, with a speech very
   soft, very low—
" The ways will be long, but the days will be long,"
   quoth the river,
" To me a long liver, long, long ! " quoth the river—
   the river.

I dreamed of the country that night, of the orchard,
   the sky,
The voice that had mocked coming after and over and
   under.
But at last—in a day or two namely—Eleven and I
Were very fast friends, and to him I confided the
   wonder.
He said that was Echo. " Was Echo a wise kind of bee
That had learned how to laugh : could it laugh in one's
   ear and then fly,
And laugh again yonder ? "   " No ;   Echo "—he
   whispered it low—
" Was a woman, they said, but a woman whom no
   one could see
And no one could find ; and he did not believe it,
   not he,
But he could not get near for the river that held us
   asunder

Yet I that had money—a shilling, a whole silver
    shilling—
We might cross if I thought I would spend it." "Oh,
    yes, I was willing "—
And we ran hand in hand, we ran down to the ferry,
    the ferry,
And we heard how she mocked at the folk with a
    voice clear and merry
When they called for the ferry; but oh! she was
    very—was very
Swift-footed. She spoke and was gone; and when
    Oliver cried,
"Hie over! hie over! you man of the ferry—the ferry!"
By the still water's side she was heard far and wide—
    she replied,
And she mocked in her voice sweet and merry, "You
    man of the ferry!
You man of—you man of the ferry!"

"Hie over!" he shouted. The ferryman came at his
    calling,
Across the clear reed-bordered river he ferried us fast;—
Such a chase! Hand in hand, foot to foot, we ran on;
    it surpassed
All measure her doubling—so close, then so far away
    falling,
Then gone, and no more. Oh! to see her but once
    unaware,
And the mouth that had mocked, but we might not
    (yet sure she was there!),
Nor behold her wild eyes and her mystical coun-
    tenance fair.
We sought in the wood, and we found the wood-wren
    in her stead;
In the field, and we found but the cuckoo that talked
    overhead;
By the brook, and we found the reed-sparrow deep-
    nested, in brown—

Not Echo, fair Echo! for Echo, sweet Echo! was
    flown.

So we came to the place where the dead people wait
    till God call—
The church was among them, grey moss over roof,
    over wall.
Very silent, so low. And we stood on a green grassy
    mound
And looked in at a window, for Echo, perhaps in her
    round
Might have come in to hide there. But no ; every
    oak carven seat
Was empty. We saw the great Bible—old, old, very
    old,
And the parson's great Prayer-book beside it ; we
    heard the slow beat
Of the pendulum swing in the tower ; we saw the
    clear gold
Of a sunbeam float down to the aisle and then waver
    and play
On the low chancel step and the railing, and Oliver
    said,
" Look, Katie! Look, Katie! when Lettice came
    here to be wed
She stood where that sunbeam drops down, and all
    white was her gown ;
And she stepped upon flowers they strewed for her."
    Then quoth small Seven,
" Shall I wear a white gown and have flowers to walk
    upon ever ? "

All doubtful : " It takes a long time to grow up,"
    quoth Eleven ;
" You're so little, you know, and the church is so old,
    it can never
Last on till *you're* tall." And in whispers—because
    it was old,

And holy, and fraught with strange meaning, half
   felt, but not told,
Full of old parson's prayers, who were dead, of old
   days, of old folk
Neither heard nor beheld, but about us, in whispers
   we spoke.
Then we went from it softly, and ran hand in hand
   to the strand,
While bleating of flocks and birds piping made
   sweeter the land.
And Echo came back e'en as Oliver drew to the ferry,
" O Katie ! " " O Katie ! " " Come on, then ! "
   " Come on, then ! "   " For, see,
The round sun, all red, lying low by the tree "—" by
   the tree."

" By the tree." Ay, she mocked him again, with her
   voice sweet and merry :
" Hie over ! " " Hie over ! "   " You man of the
   ferry "—" the ferry—
You man of—you man of—the ferry."

Ay, here—it was here that we woke her, the Echo of old ;
All life of that day seems an echo, and many times told.
Shall I cross by the ferry to-morrow, and come in my
   white
To that little low church ? and will Oliver meet me
   anon ?
Will it all seem an echo from childhood passed over
   —passed on ?
Will the grave parson bless us ? Hark, hark ! in the
   dim failing light
I hear her ! As then the child's voice clear and high,
   sweet and merry,
Now she mocks the man's tone with " Hie over ! Hie
   over the ferry ! "
" And Katie." " And Katie." " Art out with the
   glow-worms to-night,

My Katie ? " " My Katie." For gladness I break
    into laughter
And tears. Then it all comes again as from far-away
    years ;
Again, some one else—Oh, how softly !—with laughter
    comes after,
Comes after—with laughter comes after.

JEAN INGELOW.

There is the history of two lives in this poem ; but the
story itself is very ordinary. We must study the beautiful
way in which it is told.

What is the refrain, and what effect has it upon the
reader ?

Are there any clear pictures in the poem ? Which do
you like best ? (Sometimes there is a complete picture
in a single line.)

Study the words which describe things. Some of them
are very well chosen and full of colour.

What was the bird that was " an easy forgiver " ?

There is a *metaphor* or likeness in the line which begins
" But each rush." Study it, and try to find other likenesses. (If the word " like " or " as " is used, we call
the likeness or comparison a *simile*.)

The Eve of Bannockburn

THE Monarch rode along the van,
The foe's approaching force to scan,
His line to marshal and to range,
And ranks to square, and fronts to change.
Alone he rode—from head to heel
Sheathed in his ready arms of steel ;
Nor mounted yet on war-horse wight,
But, till more near the shock of fight,
Reining a palfrey low and light.
A diadem of gold was set

The Monarch, Robert Bruce.   *Wight,* Strong.

Above his bright steel basinet,
And clasped within its glittering twine
Was seen the glove of Argentine ;
Truncheon or leading staff he lacks,
Bearing instead a battle-axe.
He ranged his soldiers for the fight,
Accoutred thus, in open sight
Of either host.—Three bowshots far
Paused the deep front of England's war,
And rested on their arms awhile
To close and rank their warlike file,
And hold high council, if that night
Should view the strife, or dawning light.

Oh, gay yet fearful to behold,
Flashing with steel and rough with gold,
    And bristled o'er with bills and spears,
With plumes and pennons waving fair
Was that bright battle front ! for there
    Rode England's King and peers !
And who that saw that Monarch ride,
His kingdom battled by his side,
Could then his direful doom foretell !
Fair was his seat in knightly selle,
And in his sprightly eye was set
Some spark of the Plantagenet.
Though light and wandering was his glance,
It flashed at sight of shield and lance.
" Know'st thou," he said, " De Argentine,
Yon knight who marshals thus their line ? "—
" The tokens on his helmet tell

Glove of Argentine. Sir Giles de Argentine, one of the most ac-
complished knights of his time, had been sent as an ambassador
from Edward to keep the Western Isles loyal to him. Meeting
Bruce there, he claimed him as a prisoner, but this the Lord of the
Isles forbade. Argentine then gave Bruce his glove to wear as a
token of challenge till they met in battle.

His direful doom. Edward II. was murdered in Berkeley Castle,
September 21, 1327.

Selle, French for a saddle.

The Bruce, my Liege ; I know him well."—
" And shall the audacious traitor brave
The presence where our banners wave ? "—
" So please my Liege," said Argentine,
" Were he but horsed on steed like mine,
To give him fair and knightly chance,
I would adventure forth my lance."—
" In battle-day," the King replied,
" Nice tourney rules are set aside.
—Still must the rebel dare our wrath ?
Set on him, sweep him from our path ! "
And, at King Edward's signal, soon
Dashed from the ranks Sir Henry Boune.

Of Hereford's high blood he came,
A race renowned for knightly fame.
He burned before his Monarch's eye
To do some deed of chivalry.
He spurred his steed, he couched his lance,
And darted on the Bruce at once.
—As motionless as rocks that bide
The wrath of the advancing tide,
The Bruce stood fast.—Each breast beat high,
And dazzled was each gazing eye :
The heart had scarcely time to think,
The eyelid scarce had time to wink,
While on the King, like flash of flame,
Spurred to full speed the war-horse came !
The partridge may the falcon mock,
If that slight palfrey stand the shock :
But, swerving from the knight's career,
Just as they met, Bruce shunned the spear.
Onward the baffled warrior bore
His course—but soon his course was o'er.
High in his stirrups stood the King,
And gave his battle-axe the swing.
Right on De Boune, the whiles he passed,
Fell that stern dint—the first, the last !

Such strength upon the blow was put
The helmet crashed like hazel-nut ;
The axe-shaft, with its brazen clasp,
Was shivered to the gauntlet grasp.
Springs from the blow the startled horse,
Drops to the plain the lifeless corse.
—First of that fatal field, how soon,
How sudden, fell the fierce De Boune !
One pitying glance the Monarch sped,
Where on the field his foe lay dead ;
Then gently turned his palfrey's head,
And, pacing back his sober way,
Slowly he gained his own array.
There round their King the leaders crowd,
And blame his recklessness aloud,
That risked, 'gainst each adventurous spear,
A life so valued and so dear.
His broken weapon's shaft surveyed
The King, and careless answer made,
" My loss may pay my folly's tax ;
I've broke my trusty battle-axe."

SIR WALTER SCOTT.

The line used in this poem seems to me to recall the
movement of a horse. Is it galloping or ambling ?
Does the movement change in any part of the poem ?
Are the lines all of the same length ?

Try the measure to describe part of the Battle of
Crecy, in lines of a similar kind. Here is the story :

The English line was in two divisions. In each of the
divisions there were about two thousand archers and
eight hundred men-at-arms. The archers in each division were drawn up on the flank of the men-at-arms,
and were arranged like the points of a harrow, so that
each man in the second line could shoot between two of
the first. King Philip had an army five or six times as
strong as that of the English, and it consisted almost
wholly of horse-soldiers in armour. In front of his line
of mailed knights were Genoese cross-bowmen.

The cross-bowmen began the battle, but they were almost useless against the English archers. Their bow-strings had been wetted and made slack by the rain, while those of the English had been kept dry. At its best the cross-bow was a clumsy weapon. While the Genoese was winding up his bow for a single shot, the English archer could fire half a dozen arrows. The long-bow had also a longer range, so that the cross-bowmen were shot down and dispersed before they were able to do much mischief.

Then the knights advanced, riding through or over the routed cross-bowmen. At once the English archers began to fire long, steady volleys at the advancing line. Down went men and horses in great confusion. Soon a great heap of wounded and dead lay before the English, and this ghastly barrier prevented the knights from riding them down. Only here and there did the French-men come to hand strokes with the English men-at-arms.

For some hours the battle surged along the English front, while the arrows whistled through the air with deadly effect, and in such numbers that " it seemed as if it snowed." At nightfall the French knights fled, leaving a quarter of their whole army dead or dying on the stricken field. Thus the battle was won, and the archers had not moved a single pace from their first position.

The Heart of Bruce

[The " Good Lord James," Earl of Douglas, on his way to the Holy Land with the heart of the Bruce in a casket, felt it his sacred duty to assist Alphonso, King of Leon and Castile, who was at war with the Moorish governor of Granada. The battle described was fought on the borders of the province of Andalusia, in the south of Spain, 1329.]

THE trumpets blew, the crossbolts flew,
    The arrows flashed like flame,
As spur in side, and spear in rest,
    Against the foe we came.

And many a bearded Saracen
    Went down, both horse and man ;
For through their ranks we rode like corn,
    So furiously we ran !

But in behind our path they closed,
    Though fain to let us through,
For they were forty thousand men,
    And we were wondrous few.

We might not see a lance's length,
    So dense was their array,
But the long fell sweep of the Scottish blade
    Still held them hard at bay.

" Make in, make in ! " Lord Douglas cried,
    " Make in, my brethren dear !
Sir William of St. Clair is down ;
    We may not leave him here ! "

But thicker, thicker grew the swarm,
    And sharper shot the rain,
And the horses reared amid the press,
    But they would not charge again.

" Now Jesu help thee," said Lord James,
    " Thou kind and true St. Clair !
And if I may not bring thee off,
    I'll die beside thee there ! "

Then in his stirrup up he stood,
    So lion-like and bold,
And held the precious heart aloft
    All in its case of gold.

He flung it from him, far ahead,
    And never spake he more,
But—" Pass thee first, thou dauntless heart,
    As thou wert wont of yore ! "

The roar of fight rose fiercer yet,
   And heavier still the stour,
Till the spears of Spain came shivering in,
   And swept away the Moor.

" Now praised be God, the day is won !
   They fly o'er flood and fell—
Why dost thou draw the rein so hard,
   Good Knight, that fought so well ? "—

" Oh, ride ye on, Lord King ! " he said,
   " And leave the dead to me,
For I must keep the dreariest watch
   That ever I shall dree !

" There lies, beside his master's heart,
   The Douglas, stark and grim ;
And woe is me I should be here,
   Not side by side with him !

" The world grows cold, my arm is old,
   And thin my lyart hair,
And all that I loved best on earth
   Is stretched before me there.

" O Bothwell banks ! that bloom so bright
   Beneath the sun of May,
The heaviest cloud that ever blew
   Is bound for you this day."

The King he lighted from his horse,
   He flung his brand away,
And took the Douglas by the hand,
   So stately as he lay :

" God give thee rest, thou valiant soul,
   That fought so well for Spain ;

Dree, Suffer or endure.   *Lyart*, Growing grey.

I'd rather half my land were gone,
   So thou wert here again."

We bore the good Lord James away,
   And the priceless heart he bore,
And heavily we steered our ship
   Towards the Scottish shore.

We laid our chief in Douglas Kirk,
   The heart in fair Melróse ;
And woeful men we were that day.—
   God grant their souls repose !

                              W. E. AYTOUN.

Aytoun, like Sir Walter Scott, greatly admired the old
ballad, but he called his own story-poems " lays." The
word " lay " strictly means a short poem meant to be
sung. The old ballad, too, was meant to be sung or
recited in a kind of sing-song to the music of a harp
played by a gleeman or minstrel.

Does this poem resemble an old ballad in any way ?

The heart of the Bruce is said to have been buried
under the high altar of Melrose Abbey.

A Ballad of Pentyre Town

FOAM flies white over rocks of black,
   Nights are dark when the boats go down ;
But souls flit back in the wild wind's track,
   And grey gulls gather in Pentyre Town.

Wild, grey gulls in the narrow street,
   Wheeling, wavering, to and fro,
(Dear the echo of vanished feet !)
   Flocking in as the sun sinks low.

Pale she stands at her open door,
   (Dark little streets of a fishing town ;)

Shrill, thin voices from sea and shore
   Fill the air as the sun goes down.

" Out and alas for my woe ! " saith she,
   (See how the grey gulls whirl and throng !)
" Love ! come back from the weary sea ! "
   (Sore is sorrow and hours are long.)

One comes sailing with outstretched beak,
   White throat lifted in wailing cry,
Stoops his wing, to a woman's cheek,
   Swift and light, as he wavers by.

Foam flies white over rocks of black,
   Nights are dark when the boats go down,
But souls flit back in the wild wind's track,
   And grey gulls gather in Pentyre Town.

Still she stands at her open door,
   (Flickering sunrays faint and far,)
" Woe is heavy and doubt is sore,"
   (Sobbing waves on the dull Doom Bar.)

" Sleep flees far from mine eyes," saith she,
   (Skies are wild with the rough wind's breath,)
" All for my love's voice calling me,"
   (Robbed Love clings at the knees of Death.)

Now she strays on the wind-swept strand,
   " Fair our wandering days shall be ! "
Sets her foot on the wan, wet sand,
   (Faint feet falter, but wings flash free.)

" Love, I come to your call at last."
   (Black boats lean on the low sea-shore.)
" Fear and doubting are overpast,"
   (Set the tiller, and grasp the oar !)

No boat stirs on the sea's dark breast,
   (Long clouds writhe on a pallid sky,)
Storm-winds wail to the lurid west,
   Sad and shrill as a sea-bird's cry.

Foam flies white over rocks of black,
   Daylight dies, and a boat goes down ;
But souls flit back in the wild wind's track,
   And grey gulls gather in Pentyre Town.

                ROSAMUND MARRIOTT WATSON.

Is this an old ballad or a ballad-poem of to-day ? How
can you tell ?
Where are the repetitions ?
Find a sharp contrast in colour (which is repeated).
Read the poem aloud with one other person, who will
take the part of " she."
Read slowly and solemnly. By the way, *could* the
lines be read swiftly ? If not, why not ?

Edinburgh after Flodden

NEWS of battle ! news of battle !
   Hark ! 'tis ringing down the street ;
And the archways and the pavement
   Bear the clang of hurrying feet.
News of battle ! who hath brought it ?
   News of triumph ! who should bring
Tidings from our noble army,
   Greetings from our gallant King ?
All last night we watched the beacons
   Blazing on the hills afar,
Each one bearing, as it kindled,
   Message of the opened war.
All night long the northern streamers
   Shot across the trembling sky—
Fearful lights, that never beacon
   Save when kings or heroes die.

News of battle ! who hath brought it ?
   All are thronging to the gate :
" Warder—warder ! open quickly !
   Man, is this a time to wait ? "
And the heavy gates are opened :
   Then a murmur long and loud,
And a cry of fear and wonder
   Bursts from out the bending crowd.
For they see in battered harness
   Only one hard-stricken man,
And his weary steed is wounded,
   And his cheek is pale and wan.
Spearless hangs a bloody banner
   In his weak and drooping hand—
What ! can that be Randolph Murray,
   Captain of the city band ?

Round him crush the people, crying,
   " Tell us all—oh, tell us true !
Where are they who went to battle,
   Randolph Murray, sworn to you ?
Where are they, our brothers—children ?
   Have they met the English foe ?
Why art thou alone, unfollowed ?
   Is it weal, or is it woe ? "
Like a corpse the grisly warrior
   Looks from out his helm of steel ;
But no word he speaks in answer—
   Only with his armèd heel
Chides his weary steed, and onward
   Up the city streets they ride ;
Fathers, sisters, mothers, children,
   Shrieking, praying by his side,
" By the God that made thee, Randolph !
   Tell us what mischance hath come."
Then he lifts his riven banner,
   And the asker's voice is dumb.

The elders of the city
    Have met within their hall—
The men whom good King James had charged
    To watch the tower and wall.
" Your hands are weak with age," he said,
    " Your hearts are stout and true ;
So bide ye in the Maiden Town,
    While others fight for you.
My trumpet from the Border-side
    Shall send a blast so clear,
That all who wait within the gate
    That stirring sound may hear.
Or, if it be the will of Heaven
    That back I never come,
And if, instead of Scottish shouts,
    Ye hear the English drum,—
Then let the warning bells ring out,
    Then gird you to the fray,
Then man the walls like burghers stout,
    And fight while fight you may.
'Twere better that in fiery flame
    The roofs should thunder down,
Than that the foot of foreign foe
    Should trample in the town ! "

Then in came Randolph Murray,—
    His step was slow and weak,
And, as he doffed his dinted helm,
    The tears ran down his cheek :
They fell upon his corselet,
    And on his mailèd hand,
As he gazed around him wistfully
    Leaning sorely on his brand.
And none who then beheld him
    But straight were smote with fear,
For a bolder and a sterner man
    Had never couched a spear.

They knew so sad a messenger
  Some ghastly news must bring :
And all of them were fathers,
  And their sons were with the King.

And up then rose the Provost—
  A brave old man was he,
Of ancient name, and knightly fame,
  And chivalrous degree.
He ruled our city like a lord
  Who brooked no equal here,
And for the townsmen's rights
  Stood up 'gainst prince and peer.
And he had seen the Scottish host
  March from the Borough-muir,
With music-storm and clamorous shout,
And all the din that thunders out
  When youth's of victory sure.
But yet a dearer thought had he,
  For, with a father's pride,
He saw his last remaining son
  Go forth by Randolph's side,
With casque on head and spur on heel,
  All keen to do and dare ;
And proudly did that gallant boy
  Dunedin's banner bear.
Oh, woeful now was the old man's look,
  And he spake right heavily—
" Now, Randolph, tell thy tidings,
  However sharp they be !
Woe is written on thy visage,
  Death is looking from thy face :
Speak—though it be of overthrow,
  It cannot be disgrace ! "

Right bitter was the agony
  That wrung that soldier proud :

Thrice did he strive to answer,
    And thrice he groaned aloud.
Then he gave the riven banner
    To the old man's shaking hand,
Saying—" That is all I bring ye
    From the bravest of the land !
Ay ! ye may look upon it—
    It was guarded well and long,
By your brothers and your children,
    By the valiant and the strong.
One by one they fell around it,
    As the archers laid them low,
Grimly dying, still unconquered,
    With their faces to the foe.
Ay ! ye well may look upon it—
    There is more than honour there,
Else, be sure, I had not brought it
    From the field of dark despair.
Never yet was royal banner
    Steeped in such a costly dye ;
It hath lain upon a bosom
    Where no other shroud shall lie.
Sirs ! I charge you, keep it holy,
    Keep it as a sacred thing,
For the stain ye see upon it
    Was the life-blood of your King ! "

  .   .   .   .   .

" Thou needst not tell it : he is dead.
    God help us all this day !
But speak—how fought the citizens
    Within the furious fray ?
For, by the might of Mary,
    'Twere something still to tell
That no Scottish foot went backward
    When the Royal Lion fell ! "

" No one failed him ! He is keeping
    Royal state and semblance still ;

Knight and noble lie around him
    Cold on Flodden's fatal hill.
Of the brave and gallant-hearted,
    Whom ye sent with prayers away,
Not a single man departed
    From his Monarch yesterday.
Had you seen them, O my masters !
    When the night began to fall,
And the English spearmen gathered
    Round a grim and ghastly wall !
As the wolves in winter circle
    Round the leaguer on the heath,
So the greedy foe glared upward,
    Panting still for blood and death.
But a rampart rose before them
    Which the boldest dared not scale ;
Every stone a Scottish body,
    Every step a corpse in mail !
And behind it lay our Monarch,
    Clenching still his shivered sword ;
By his side Montrose and Athole,
    At his feet a southern lord.
All so thick they lay together,
    When the stars lit up the sky,
That I knew not who were stricken,
    Or who yet remained to die.
Few there were when Surrey halted,
    And his wearied host withdrew ;
None but dying men around me,
    When the English trumpet blew.
Then I stooped and took the banner,
    As ye see it, from his breast,
And I closed our hero's eyelids,
    And I left him to his rest."

                        W. E. AYTOUN.

It is not easy to say how the poet manages to make us
feel. Of course, he has a feeling subject, which still stirs

Leaguer, Camp.

men's blood, but that is not all. His lines are clean-cut; his phrases are stirring—" News of battle!" he changes the " time " of his measure to suit the various parts of his story; and above all, he writes simply. And he wins warm sympathy for misfortune bravely borne.

This is a good measure for imitation. Any school history-book is full of subjects—*e.g.*, the story of the burghers of Calais—if you wish to try your hand at making verses.

Lucy Gray; or, Solitude

[The poem was founded on a circumstance told me by my sister, of a little girl who, not far from Halifax in Yorkshire, was bewildered in a snow-storm. Her foot-steps were traced by her parents to the middle of the lock of a canal, and no other vestige of her, backward or forward, could be traced. The body, however, was found in the canal.—WORDSWORTH.]

OFT I had heard of Lucy Gray :
    And, when I crossed the wild,
I chanced to see at break of day
    The solitary child.

No mate, no comrade Lucy knew ;
    She dwelt on a wide moor,
—The sweetest thing that ever grew
    Beside a human door !

You yet may spy the fawn at play,
    The hare upon the green ;
But the sweet face of Lucy Gray
    Will never more be seen.

" To-night will be a stormy night—
    You to the town must go ;
And take a lantern, child, to light
    Your mother through the snow."

" That, father, will I gladly do :
  'Tis scarcely afternoon—
The minster-clock has just struck two,
  And yonder is the moon ! "

At this the father raised his hook,
  And snapped a faggot-band ;
He plied his work ;—and Lucy took
  The lantern in her hand.

Not blither is the mountain roe :
  With many a wanton stroke
Her feet disperse the powdery snow,
  That rises up like smoke.

The storm came on before its time :
  She wandered up and down ;
And many a hill did Lucy climb :
  But never reached the town.

The wretched parents all that night
  Went shouting far and wide ;
But there was neither sound nor sight
  To serve them for a guide.

At daybreak on a hill they stood
  That overlooked the moor ;
And thence they saw the bridge of wood,
  A furlong from their door.

They wept—and, turning homeward, cried,
  " In heaven we all shall meet ; "
—When in the snow the mother spied
  The print of Lucy's feet.

Then downwards from the steep hill's edge
  They tracked the footmarks small ;
And through the broken hawthorn hedge,
  And by the long stone-wall ;

And then an open field they crossed :
  The marks were still the same ;
They tracked them on, nor ever lost ;
  And to the bridge they came.

They followed from the snowy bank
  Those footmarks, one by one,
Into the middle of the plank ;
  And farther there were none !

—Yet some maintain that to this day
  She is a living child ;
That you may see sweet Lucy Gray
  Upon the lonesome wild.

O'er rough and smooth she trips along,
  And never looks behind ;
And sings a solitary song
  That whistles in the wind.

                              W. WORDSWORTH.

The note at the head of the poem gives the story of
Lucy Gray as we might find it in a newspaper. The
poem fills out the story, and makes us *feel* not only the
horror but also the sadness of the tale.

The poet uses very simple language because he is writing of simple people. Few words are spoken—especially
by the father, who goes on with his work, as he must do.

How do you reconcile the last sentence of Wordsworth's note at the head of the poem with the two
beautiful stanzas at the end ?

At all events, Lucy Gray always remained a child—
and went on living in the memory of those who had
known her.

Which parts of the poem give the sense by the sound ?

Lucy

SHE dwelt among the untrodden ways,
 Beside the springs of Dove.
A maid whom there were none to praise
 And very few to love.

A violet by a mossy stone,
 Half hidden from the eye,
Fair as a star, when only one
 Is shining in the sky.

She lived unknown, and few could know
 When Lucy ceased to be,
But she is in her grave ; and oh !
 The difference to me !

W. WORDSWORTH.

A writer says that these simple verses give the complete story of a simple outwardly uneventful life.

Read them slowly again, with this thought in your mind.

The second stanza contains two very beautiful comparisons or likenesses. In the first Lucy is *called* a violet; this is a " metaphor." In the second her beauty is said to be *like* that of a star; this is a simile. You will not find in all English poetry a lovelier metaphor and simile.

These comparisons or likenesses are some of the most beautiful things in poetry. It is not always easy to tell a metaphor from a simile, but it is safe to call either of them a comparison or likeness. The pages of this book are full of them.

The Battle of Killiecrankie

ON the heights of Killiecrankie
　　Yester-morn our army lay.
Slowly rose the mist in columns
　　From the river's broken way ;
Hoarsely roared the swollen torrent,
　　And the pass was wrapt in gloom,
When the clansmen rose together
　　From their lair amidst the broom.
Then we belted on our tartans,
　　And our bonnets down we drew,
And we felt our broadswords' edges,
　　And we proved them to be true ;
And we prayed the prayer of soldiers,
　　And we cried the gathering cry,
And we clasped the hands of kinsmen,
　　And we swore to do or die !
Then our leader rode before us,
　　On his war-horse black as night ;—
Well the Cameronian rebels
　　Knew that charger in the fight . . .
And he raised his hand for silence—
　　" Soldiers ! I have sworn a vow :
Ere the evening star shall glisten
　　On Schiehallion's lofty brow,
Either we shall rest in triumph,
　　Or another of the Graemes

Our army. Immediately after the Revolution which made
William III. and Mary II. joint rulers of the United Kingdom,
James Graham (or Graeme) of Claverhouse, Viscount Dundee,
roused the clans against William of Orange, defeating General
Mackay at the Pass of Killiecrankie on June 17, 1689. The battle
lasted only a few minutes. Graham was buried in Blair Atholl
churchyard. The story is supposed to be told by one of Graham's
followers.
Cameronian rebels. Graham had helped to hunt down the Camer-
onians, who refused to worship God in any way but their own.

Shall have died in battle harness
    For his country and King James . . .
Strike ! and drive the trembling rebels
    Backward o'er the stormy Forth ;
Let them tell their pale Convention
    How they fared within the North.
Let them tell that Highland honour
    Is not to be bought or sold,
That we scorn their Prince's anger
    As we loathe his foreign gold.
Strike ! and when the fight is over,
    If you look in vain for me,
Where the dead are lying thickest,
    Search for him that was Dundee ! " . . .
Soon we heard a challenge trumpet
    Sounding in the pass below,
And the distant tramp of horses,
    And the voices of the foe.
Down we crouched amid the bracken,
    Till the Lowland ranks drew near ;
Panting like the hounds in summer
    When they scent the stately deer.
From the dark defile emerging
    Next we saw the squadrons come,
Leslie's foot and Leven's troopers,
    Marching to the tuck of drum ;
Through the scattered wood of birches,
    O'er the broken ground and heath,
Wound the long battalion slowly,
    Till they gained the field beneath.
Then we bounded from our covert—
    Judge how looked the Saxons then,
When they saw the rugged mountain
    Start to life with armèd men !
Like a tempest down the ridges
    Swept the hurricane of steel,

King James. The second of that name, whom William III. had
succeeded.

Rose the slogan of Macdonald,
   Flashed the broadsword of Lochiel !
Vainly sped the withering volley
   'Mongst the foremost of our band,—
On we poured until we met them
   Foot to foot, and hand to hand.
Horse and man went down like driftwood
   When the floods are black at Yule,
And their carcasses are whirling
   In the Garry's deepest pool.
Horse and man went down before us,
   Living foe there tarried none
On the field of Killiecrankie
   When that stubborn fight was done.
And the evening star was shining,
   On Schiehallion's distant head,
When we wiped our bloody broadswords
   And returned to count the dead.
There we found him, gashed and gory,
   Stretched upon the cumbered plain,
As he told us where to seek him,
   In the thickest of the slain.
And a smile was on his visage,
   For within his dying ear
Pealed the joyful note of triumph,
   And the clansmen's clamorous cheer.
So, amid the battle's thunder,
   Shot, and steel, and answering flame,
In the glory of his manhood,
   Passed the spirit of the Graeme !

                W. E. AYTOUN.

   This is another stirring lay, rushing along in a manner almost breathless, like the stream in the narrow pass where the battle was fought.

   History blames Graham of Claverhouse for many cruel deeds, but he died like a brave man, fighting for the prince whom he reckoned ought to be on the throne.

       Garry, A tributary of the Tay.

Who is supposed to be telling the story?

Try to write a portion of the story of Trafalgar in this measure.   You might begin:

" Off the coasts of proud Hispania."

Bernardo and Alphonso

WITH some good ten of his chosen men, Bernardo
    hath appeared,
Before them all, in the palace hall, the lying King to
    beard;
With cap in hand and eye on ground, he came in
    reverent guise,
But ever and anon he frowned, and flame broke from
    his eyes.

" A curse upon thee," cries the King, " who com'st
    unbid to me;
But what from traitor's blood should spring save
    traitor like to thee?
His sire, lords, had a traitor's heart; perchance our
    champion brave
May think it were a pious part to share Don Sancho's
    grave."

" Whoever told this tale the King hath rashness to
    repeat,"
Cries Bernard, " here my gage I fling before the liar's
    feet!
No treason was in Sancho's blood, no stain in mine
    doth lie—
Below the throne, what knight will own the coward
    calumny?

" The blood that I like water shed, when Roland did
    advance,
By secret traitors hired and led, to make us slaves of
    France;—

The life of King Alphonso I saved at Roncesval—
Your words, Lord King, are recompense abundant for
    it all !

" Your horse was down,—your hope was flown,—I saw
    the falchion shine
That soon had drunk your royal blood, had I not ven-
    tured mine ;
But memory soon of service done deserteth the ingrate,
And you've thanked the son for life and crown by the
    father's bloody fate.

" You swore upon your kingly faith to set Don
    Sancho free,
But, curse upon your paltering breath ! the light he
    ne'er did see ;
He died in dungeon cold and dim, by Alphonso's base
    decree,
And visage blind and stiffened limb were all they gave
    to me.

" The King that swerveth from his word hath stained
    his purple black—
No Spanish lord will draw the sword behind a liar's
    back ;
But noble vengeance shall be mine ; an open hate I'll
    show—
The King hath injured Carpio's line, and Bernard is
    his foe."

" Seize—seize him ! " loud the King doth scream.
    " There are a thousand here—
Let his foul blood this instant stream—what ! caitiffs,
    do you fear ?
Seize—seize the traitor ! " But not one to move a
    finger dareth,—
Bernardo standeth by the throne, and calm his sword
    he bareth.

He drew the falchion from the sheath and held it up
    on high,
And all the hall was still as death ; cries Bernard,
    " Here am I ;
And here's the sword that owns no lord, excepting
    Heaven and me ;
Fain would I know who dares its point—King, Condé,
    or Grandee ? "

Then to his mouth the horn he drew—(it hung below
    his cloak)—
His ten true men the signal knew, and through the
    ring they broke ;
With helm on head and blade in hand, the knights the
    circle brake ;
And back the lordlings 'gan to stand, and the false
    King to quake.

" Ha ! Bernard," quoth Alphonso, " what means this
    warlike guise ?
You know full well I jested—you know your worth I
    prize."
But Bernard turned upon his heel, and smiling passed
    away ;
Long rued Alphonso and Castille the jesting of that
    day.

J. G. LOCKHART.

Bernardo's Revenge

WHAT tents gleam on the green hillside, like snow in
    the sunny beam,
What gloomy warriors gather there, like a surly moun-
    tain stream ?
These, for Bernardo's vengeance, have come like a
    stormy blast,
The rage of their long-cherished hate on a cruel king
    to cast.

" Smiters of tyranny ! " cries their chief, " see yonder
    slavish host,
We shall drench the field with their craven blood, or
    freedom's hopes were lost ;
You know I come for a father's death, my filial vow
    to pay,
Then let the " Murdered Sancho ! " be your battle-
    cry to-day.

" On, on ! for the death of the tyrant king ! "
    " Hurrah ! " was the answering cry ;
" We follow thee to victory, or follow thee to die ! "
The battlefield,—the charge,—the shock,—the quiver-
    ing struggle now,—
The rout,—the shout !—while lightnings flash from
    Bernardo's angry brow.

The chieftain's arm has need of rest, his brand drips
    red with gore,
But one last sacrifice remains, ere his work of toil is
    o'er.
The King, who looked for victory from his large and
    well-trained host,
Now flies for safety from the field, where all his hopes
    are lost ;

But full in front, with blood-red sword, a warrior
    appears,
And the war-cry, " Murdered Sancho ! " rings in the
    tyrant's ears.
" Ha ! noble King, have we met at last ? " with
    scornful lip he cries :
" Don Sancho's son would speak with you once more
    before he dies ;

" Your kindness to my sainted sire is graven on my
    heart,
And I would show my gratitude once more before we
    part.

Draw ! for the last of Sancho's race is ready for your
    sword ;—
Bernardo's blood should flow by him, by whom his
    sire's was poured !

" What wait you for, vile, craven wretch ? it was not
    thus you stood
When laying out your fiendish plans to spill my
    father's blood.
Draw ! for I will not learn from thee the assassin's
    coward trade,
I scorn the lesson you have taught—unsheathe your
    murderous blade ! "

Roused by Bernardo's fiery taunts, the King at length
    engaged :
He fought for life, but all in vain ; unequal strife he
    waged !
Bernardo's sword has pierced his side—the tyrant's
    reign is o'er,—
" Father, I have fulfilled my vow, I thirst for blood no
    more."

UNKNOWN.

This story belongs to the early days, to the time of
Charlemagne (742–814), whose great leader Roland is
spoken of in the fourth stanza. At Roncesval, a pass in
the Pyrenees, the army of Charlemagne, under Roland,
was overtaken by the Moors of Spain and cut to pieces,
Roland being slain.

The two poems tell us a tale of anger, passion, and
revenge, suitable to the time when men's chief occupation
was war. The question is, do the two writers tell the
story vigorously, with force and strength ? Can you
hear the rattle of armour and weapons and the tramp of
horses in the line used by the poets ?

If so, you might use the line to describe one of our own
battles, say Waterloo, or, better still, Agincourt, par-
ticulars of which you can obtain from your history book.

Goody Blake and Harry Gill

A TRUE STORY

OH ! what's the matter ? what's the matter ?
What is't that ails young Harry Gill ?
That evermore his teeth they chatter,
Chatter, chatter, chatter still !
Of waistcoats Harry has no lack,
Good duffle grey, and flannel fine ;
He has a blanket on his back,
And coats enough to smother nine.

In March, December, and in July,
'Tis all the same with Harry Gill ;
The neighbours tell, and tell you truly,
His teeth they chatter, chatter still.
At night, at morning, and at noon,
'Tis all the same with Harry Gill ;
Beneath the sun, beneath the moon,
His teeth they chatter, chatter still !

Young Harry was a lusty drover,
And who so stout of limb as he ?
His cheeks were red as ruddy clover ;
His voice was like the voice of three.
Old Goody Blake was old and poor ;
Ill fed she was, and thinly clad ;
And any man who passed her door
Might see how poor a hut she had.

All day she spun in her poor dwelling :
And then her three hours' work at night
Alas ! 'twas hardly worth the telling,
It would not pay for candle-light.
Remote from sheltered village green,
On a hill's northern side she dwelt,

Where from sea-blasts the hawthorns lean,
And hoary dews are slow to melt.

By the same fire to boil their pottage,
Two poor old dames, as I have known,
Will often live in one small cottage ;
But she, poor woman ! housed alone.
'Twas well enough when summer came,
The long, warm, lightsome summer-day.
Then at her door the *canty* dame
Would sit, as any linnet, gay.

But when the ice our streams did fetter,
Oh then how her old bones would shake !
You would have said, if you had met her,
'Twas a hard time for Goody Blake.
Her evenings then were dull and dead :
Sad case it was, as you may think,
For very cold to go to bed ;
And then for cold not sleep a wink.

O joy for her ! whene'er in winter
The winds at night had made a rout ;
And scattered many a lusty splinter
And many a rotten bough about.
Yet never had she, well or sick,
As every man who knew her says,
A pile beforehand, turf or stick,
Enough to warm her for three days.

Now, when the frost was past enduring,
And made her poor old bones to ache,
Could anything be more alluring
Than an old hedge to Goody Blake ?
And now and then, it must be said,
When her old bones were cold and chill,
She left her fire, or left her bed,
To seek the hedge of Harry Gill.

Now Harry he had long suspected
This trespass of old Goody Blake ;
And vowed that she should be detected—
That he on her would vengeance take.
And oft from his warm fire he'd go,
And to the fields his road would take ;
And there, at night, in frost and snow,
He watched to seize old Goody Blake.

And once, behind a rick of barley,
Thus looking out did Harry stand :
The moon was full and shining clearly,
And crisp with frost the stubble land.
—He hears a noise—he's all awake—
Again !—on tip-toe down the hill
He softly creeps—'tis Goody Blake ;
She's at the hedge of Harry Gill !

Right glad was he when he beheld her ;
Stick after stick did Goody pull :
He stood behind a bush of elder,
Till she had filled her apron full.
When with her load she turned about,
The by-way back again to take ;
He started forward, with a shout,
And sprang upon poor Goody Blake.

And fiercely by the arm he took her,
And by the arm he held her fast,
And fiercely by the arm he shook her,
And cried, " I've caught you then at last ! "—
Then Goody, who had nothing said,
Her bundle from her lap let fall ;
And, kneeling on the sticks, she prayed
To God that is the judge of all.

She prayed, her withered hand uprearing,
While Harry held her by the arm—

" God ! who art never out of hearing,
Oh, may he never more be warm ! "
The cold, cold moon above her head,
Thus on her knees did Goody pray ;
Young Harry heard what she had said :
And icy cold he turned away.

He went complaining all the morrow
That he was cold and very chill :
His face was gloom, his heart was sorrow,
Alas ! that day for Harry Gill !
That day he wore a riding-coat,
But not a whit the warmer he :
Another was on Thursday brought,
And ere the Sabbath he had three.

'Twas all in vain, a useless matter,
And blankets were about him pinned ;
Yet still his jaws and teeth they chatter ;
Like a loose casement in the wind.
And Harry's flesh it fell away ;
And all who see him say, 'tis plain,
That, live as long as live he may,
He never will be warm again.

No word to any man he utters,
A-bed or up, to young or old ;
But ever to himself he mutters,
" Poor Harry Gill is very cold."
A-bed or up, by night or day ;
His teeth they chatter, chatter still,
Now think, ye farmers all, I pray,
Of Goody Blake and Harry Gill !

W. WORDSWORTH.

What is the refrain of this poem and what sound does it
suggest ?

This is another simple country story. Is it told in a
particularly simple manner ?

We have seen that Wordsworth was good at comparisons. Are there any suitable ones in this poem ? If so,
which do you think the best ?

The story makes us look round to see if the door has
been left open, and then find out whether the fire needs
poking. Of course, it served Harry right, but we wish he
and Goody could both be made comfortable and cosy.

Try to write a stanza (or even two) putting things
right.

Boadicea

AN ODE

WHEN the British warrior queen,
   Bleeding from the Roman rods,
Sought, with an indignant mien,
   Counsel of her country's gods,

Sage beneath a spreading oak
   Sat the Druid, hoary chief,
Every burning word he spoke
   Full of rage and full of grief :

" Princess ! if our agèd eyes
   Weep upon thy matchless wrongs,
'Tis because resentment ties
   All the terrors of our tongues.

" Rome shall perish—write that word
   In the blood that she has spilt ;
Perish hopeless and abhorred,
   Deep in ruin as in guilt.

" Rome, for empire far renowned,
   Tramples on a thousand states ;
Soon her pride shall kiss the ground,—
   Hark ! the Gaul is at her gates.

" Other Romans shall arise,
    Heedless of a soldier's name,
Sounds, not arms, shall win the prize,
    Harmony the path to fame.

" Then the progeny that springs
    From the forests of our land,
Armed with thunder, clad with wings,
    Shall a wider world command.

" Regions Cæsar never knew
    Thy posterity shall sway,
Where his eagles never flew,
    None invincible as they."

Such the bard's prophetic words,
    Pregnant with celestial fire,
Bending as he swept the chords
    Of his sweet but awful lyre.

She, with all a monarch's pride,
    Felt them in her bosom glow,
Rushed to battle, fought and died,
    Dying, hurled them at the foe.

" Ruffians, pitiless as proud,
    Heaven awards the vengeance due ;
Empire is on us bestowed,
    Shame and ruin wait for you ! "

WILLIAM COWPER.

Refresh your memory by reading the story of Boadicea in your history book, and then find out whether Cowper read the same story, and whether he has added to it.

He has written a very neat, tidy poem. Not a word is wasted. The accents fall with regular beat. The tone is lofty and dignified. The Druid speaks as a prophet, though it was, of course, very easy for the poet to make him do so !

Use the stanza for a poem (or part of one) on Magna
Charta. Make Stephen Langton speak to the barons
about the promises which King John is to be forced to
make at Runnymede.

The Loss of the *Royal George*

TOLL for the brave,
The brave that are no more !
All sunk beneath the wave,
Fast by their native shore !

Eight hundred of the brave
Whose courage well was tried,
Had made the vessel heel
And laid her on her side.

A land-breeze shook the shrouds,
And she was overset ;
Down went the *Royal George*,
With all her crew complete.

Toll for the brave !
Brave Kempenfelt is gone ;
His last sea-fight is fought,
His work of glory done.

It was not in the battle ;
No tempest gave the shock ;
She sprang no fatal leak,
She ran upon no rock.

His sword was in its sheath,
His fingers held the pen,
When Kempenfelt went down
With twice four hundred men.

—Weigh the vessel up
Once dreaded by our foes !
And mingle with our cup
The tear that England owes.

Her timbers yet are sound,
And she may float again
Full charged with England's thunder,
And plough the distant main :

But Kempenfelt is gone,
His victories are o'er,
And he and his eight hundred
Shall plough the wave no more.

W. COWPER.

The *Royal George*, while being repaired in Portsmouth harbour, was overturned on the morning of August 29, 1782. The total loss of life was about one thousand.

A Court Martial was held after the disaster, but the minutes were not published till 1922. While the workmen were busy on the heeled-up vessel two loud cracks were heard, and the ship suddenly sank because " some material part of her frame gave way, which can only be accounted for by the general state of *the decay of her timbers.*"

Where is Cowper wrong ?

The Battle of the Baltic

Of Nelson and the North
Sing the glorious day's renown,
When to battle fierce came forth
All the might of Denmark's crown,
And her arms along the deep proudly shone ;
By each gun the lighted brand
In a bold determined hand,
And the Prince of all the land
Led them on.

Like leviathans afloat
Lay their bulwarks on the brine ;
While the sign of battle flew
On the lofty British line :
It was ten of April morn by the chime :
As they drifted on their path
There was silence deep as death ;
And the boldest held his breath
For a time.

But the might of England flushed
To anticipate the scene ;
And her van the fleeter rushed
O'er the deadly space between.
" Hearts of oak ! " our captains cried, when each
    gun
From its adamantine lips
Spread a death-shade round the ships,
Like the hurricane eclipse
Of the sun.

Again ! again ! again !
And the havoc did not slack,
Till a feeble cheer the Dane
To our cheering sent us back ;—
Their shots along the deep slowly boom :—
Then ceased—and all is wail,
As they strike the shattered sail ;
Or, in conflagration pale,
Light the gloom.

Out spoke the victor then
As he hailed them o'er the wave,
" Ye are brothers ! ye are men !
And we conquer but to save ;
So peace instead of death let us bring ;
But yield, proud foe, thy fleet,
With the crews, at England's feet,

And make submission meet
To our King."

Then Denmark blessed our chief
That he gave her wounds repose ;
And the sounds of joy and grief
From her people wildly rose,
As death withdrew his shades from the day :
While the sun looked smiling bright
O'er a wide and woeful sight,
Where the fires of funeral light
Died away.

Now joy, old England, raise !
For the tidings of thy might,
By the festal cities' blaze,
Whilst the wine-cup shines in light ;
And yet amidst that joy and uproar,
Let us think of them that sleep
Full many a fathom deep
By thy wild and stormy steep,
Elsinore !

Brave hearts ! to Britain's pride
Once so faithful and so true,
On the deck of fame that died
With the gallant, good Riou :
Soft sigh the winds of heaven o'er their grave !
While the billow mournful rolls,
And the mermaid's song condoles,
Singing glory to the souls
Of the brave !   T. CAMPBELL.

Why has the poet taken great care to make his verses
sound loudly ? Select some of the best booming lines
and two or three quiet ones, by way of contrast.

Note the effective beginning and ending.

Is there any ill-feeling in the verses, or any boastful-
ness ?

Rosabelle

O LISTEN, listen, ladies gay !
  No haughty feat of arms I tell ;
Soft is the note and sad the lay
  That mourns the lovely Rosabelle.

" Moor, moor the barge, ye gallant crew !
  And, gentle ladye, deign to stay !
Rest thee in Castle Ravensheuch,
  Nor tempt the stormy firth to-day.

" The blackening wave is edged with white ;
  To inch and rock the sea-mews fly ;
The fishers have heard the water-sprite,
  Whose screams forebode that wreck is nigh.

" Last night the gifted seer did view
  A wet shroud swathed round ladye gay ;
Then stay thee, Fair, in Ravensheuch ;
  Why cross the gloomy firth to-day ? "

" 'Tis not because Lord Lindesay's heir
  To-night at Roslin leads the ball,
But that my ladye-mother there
  Sits lonely in her castle-hall.

" 'Tis not because the ring they ride,
  And Lindesay at the ring rides well,
But that my sire the wine will chide
  If 'tis not filled by Rosabelle."

—O'er Roslin all that dreary night
  A wondrous blaze was seen to gleam ;
'Twas broader than the watch-fire's light,
  And redder than the bright moonbeam.

It glared on Roslin's castled rock,
  It ruddied all the copsewood glen ;
'Twas seen from Dryden's groves of oak,
  And seen from caverned Hawthornden.

Seemed all on fire that chapel proud
  Where Roslin's chiefs uncoffined lie,
Each baron, for a sable shroud,
  Sheathed in his iron panoply.

Seemed all on fire within, around,
  Deep sacristy and altar's pale ;
Shone every pillar foliage-bound,
  And glimmered all the dead men's mail.

Blazed battlement and pinnet high,
  Blazed every rose-carved buttress fair—
So still they blaze, when fate is nigh
  The lordly line of high Saint Clair.

There are twenty of Roslin's barons bold
  Lie buried within that proud chapelle ;
Each one the holy vault doth hold—
  But the sea holds lovely Rosabelle.

And each Saint Clair was buried there,
  With candle, with book, and with knell
But the sea-caves rung and the wild winds sung
  The dirge of lovely Rosabelle.

SIR WALTER SCOTT.

This is an eerie, creepy, ghostly piece, full of pictures
rich in colour.
In which stanza does the lady begin to speak ?

The Burial of Sir John Moore after Corunna

Not a drum was heard, not a funeral note,
　As his corse to the rampart we hurried ;
Not a soldier discharged his farewell shot
　O'er the grave where our hero we buried.

We buried him darkly at dead of night,
　The sods with our bayonets turning,
By the struggling moonbeam's misty light
　And the lanthorn dimly burning.

No useless coffin enclosed his breast,
　Not in sheet or in shroud we wound him ;
But he lay like a warrior taking his rest,
　With his martial cloak around him.

Few and short were the prayers we said,
　And we spoke not a word of sorrow ;
But we steadfastly gazed on the face that was dead,
　And we bitterly thought of the morrow.

We thought, as we hollowed his narrow bed
　And smoothed down his lonely pillow,
That the foe and the stranger would tread o'er his head
　And we far away on the billow !

Lightly they'll talk of the spirit that's gone,
　And o'er his cold ashes upbraid him—
But little he'll reck, if they let him sleep on
　In the grave where a Briton has laid him.

But half of our heavy task was done
　When the clock struck the hour for retiring ;
And we heard the distant and random gun
　That the foe was sullenly firing.

Slowly and sadly we laid him down,
  From the field of his fame fresh and gory ;
We carved not a line, and we raised not a stone,
  But we left him alone with his glory.

CHARLES WOLFE.

  Look up the Battle of Corunna in your history book ;
but remember that there is something better than his-
torical facts in this poem.   What do you think it is ?
  Study the language of the verses ?   Is the meaning al-
ways clear ?   Are the lines smooth-sounding or rough ?
  Is the poem serious, sad, melancholy, miserable,
gloomy, hopeless, inspiring, proud, dignified, or savage ?
Or is it more than one of these things ?
  Study the phrases.   Which do you like best ?
  Why is this a good poem for reading aloud ?
  Does the poem suggest a picture ?   If so, indicate
roughly how it ought to be composed.
  There is character in words which can be discovered if
we linger over them—such words as home, brother, glory,
sorrow, warrior, love, joy, peace hope.   What other
words appeal to you ?

Horatius at the Bridge

[Tarquinius Superbus (also known as Sextus), the last
of the kings of ancient Rome, driven from the city by his
people for his wickedness, took refuge in Etruria with
Lars Porsena, who raised an army in support of Sextus
and marched on Rome.   We begin where they have
almost reached the bridge crossing the Tiber and leading
into the city.   The defenders are led by the chief magis-
trate, known as the Consul.]

  BUT the Consul's brow was sad,
    And the Consul's speech was low,
  And darkly looked he at the wall,
    And darkly at the foe.

" Their van will be upon us
    Before the bridge goes down ;
And if they once may win the bridge,
    What hope to save the town ? "

Then out spake brave Horatius,
    The Captain of the Gate :
" To every man upon this earth
    Death cometh soon or late.
And how can man die better
    Than facing fearful odds,
For the ashes of his fathers,
    And the temples of his Gods.

" And for the tender mother
    Who dandled him to rest,
And for the wife who nurses
    His baby at her breast,
And for the holy maidens
    Who feed the eternal flame,
To save them from false Sextus,
    That wrought the deed of shame ?

" Hew down the bridge, Sir Consul,
    With all the speed ye may ;
I, with two more to help me,
    Will hold the foe in play.
In yon strait path a thousand
    May well be stopped by three.
Now who will stand on either hand,
    And keep the bridge with me ? "

Then out spake Spurius Lartius ;
    A Ramnian proud was he :
" Lo, I will stand at thy right hand,
    And keep the bridge with thee."

The holy maidens, The Vestal Virgins who kept alight the
sacred fire of Vesta, the goddess of the hearth, in her temple.

And out spake strong Herminius ;
   Of Titian blood was he :
" I will abide on thy left side,
   And keep the bridge with thee."

" Horatius," quoth the Consul,
   " As thou sayest, so let it be."
And straight against that great array
   Forth went the dauntless Three.
For Romans in Rome's quarrel
   Spared neither land nor gold,
Nor son nor wife, nor limb nor life,
   In the brave days of old.

Then none was for a party ;
   Then all were for the state ;
Then the great man helped the poor,
   And the poor man loved the great :
Then lands were fairly portioned ;
   Then spoils were fairly sold :
The Romans were like brothers
   In the brave days of old.

Now while the Three were tightening
   Their harness on their backs,
The Consul was the foremost man
   To take in hand an axe :
And Fathers mixed with Commons,
   Seized hatchet, bar, and crow,
And smote upon the planks above
   And loosed the props below.

Meanwhile the Tuscan army,
   Right glorious to behold,
Came flashing back the noonday light,
Rank behind rank, like surges bright
   Of a broad sea of gold.

Four hundred trumpets sounded
   A peal of warlike glee,
As that great host with measured tread,
And spears advanced, and ensigns spread,
Rolled slowly towards the bridge's head,
   Where stood the dauntless Three.

The Three stood calm and silent,
   And looked upon the foes,
And a great shout of laughter
   From all the vanguard rose :
And forth three chiefs came spurring
   Before that deep array ;
To earth they sprang, their swords they drew,
And lifted high their shields, and flew
   To win the narrow way ;

Aunus from green Tifernum,
   Lord of the Hill of Vines ;
And Seius, whose eight hundred slaves
   Sicken in Ilva's mines ;
And Picus, long to Clusium
   Vassal in peace and war,
Who led to fight his Umbrian powers
From that grey crag where, girt with towers,
The fortress of Nequinum lowers
   O'er the pale waves of Nar.

Stout Lartius hurled down Aunus
   Into the stream beneath ;
Herminius struck at Seius,
   And clove him to the teeth :
At Picus brave Horatius
   Darted one fiery thrust ;
And the proud Umbrian's gilded arms
   Clashed in the bloody dust.

Then Ocnus of Falerii
　Rushed on the Roman Three ;
And Lausulus of Urgo,
　The rover of the sea ;
And Aruns of Volsinium,
　Who slew the great wild boar,
The great wild boar that had his den
　Amidst the reeds of Cosa's fen,
And wasted fields, and slaughtered men,
　Along Albinia's shore.

Herminius smote down Aruns :
　Lartius laid Ocnus low :
Right to the heart of Lausulus
　Horatius sent a blow.
" Lie there," he cried, " fell pirate !
　No more, aghast and pale,
From Ostia's walls the crowd shall mark
The track of thy destroying bark.
No more Campania's hinds shall fly
To woods and caverns when they spy
　Thy thrice-accursèd sail."

But now no sound of laughter
　Was heard among the foes.
A wild and wrathful clamour
　From all the vanguard rose.
Six spears' lengths from the entrance
　Halted that deep array,
And for a space no man came forth
　To win the narrow way.

But hark ! the cry is Astur :
　And lo ! the ranks divide ;
And the great Lord of Luna
　Comes with his stately stride.

Upon his ample shoulders
    Clangs loud the fourfold shield,
And in his hand he shakes the brand
    Which none but he can wield.

He smiled on those bold Romans
    A smile serene and high ;
He eyed the flinching Tuscans,
    And scorn was in his eye.
Quoth he, " The she-wolf's litter
    Stand savagely at bay :
But will ye dare to follow,
    If Astur clears the way ? "

Then, whirling up his broadsword
    With both hands to the height,
He rushed against Horatius,
    And smote with all his might.
With shield and blade Horatius
    Right deftly turned the blow.
The blow, though turned, came yet too nigh ;
It missed his helm, but gashed his thigh :
The Tuscans raised a joyful cry
    To see the red blood flow.

He reeled, and on Herminius
    He leaned one breathing-space ;
Then, like a wild-cat mad with wounds,
    Sprang right at Astur's face.
Through teeth, and skull, and helmet,
    So fierce a thrust he sped,
The good sword stood a hand-breadth out
    Behind the Tuscan's head.

And the great Lord of Luna
    Fell at that deadly stroke,

The she-wolf's litter. According to the ancient legend, Romulus and Remus, the ancestors of the Romans, were nursed in their infancy by a she-wolf.

As falls on Mount Alvernus
   A thunder-smitten oak.
Far o'er the crashing forest
   The giant arms lie spread ;
And the pale augurs, muttering low,
   Gaze on the blasted head.

On Astur's throat Horatius
   Right firmly pressed his heel,
And thrice and four times tugged amain,
   Ere he wrenched out the steel.
" And see," he cried, " the welcome,
   Fair guests, that waits you here !
What noble Lucumo comes next
   To taste our Roman cheer ? "

But at his haughty challenge
   A sullen murmur ran,
Mingled of wrath, and shame, and dread,
   Along that glittering van.
There lacked not men of prowess,
   Nor men of lordly race ;
For all Etruria's noblest
   Were round the fatal place.

But all Etruria's noblest
   Felt their hearts sink to see
On earth the bloody corpses,
   In the path the dauntless Three :
And, from the ghastly entrance,
   Where those bold Romans stood,
All shrank, like boys who unaware.
Ranging the woods to start a hare,
Come to the mouth of the dark lair
Where, growling low, a fierce old bear
   Lies amidst bones and blood.

Augurs, Prophets.

Was none who would be foremost
  To lead such dire attack :
But those behind cried " Forward ! "
  And those before cried " Back ! "
And backward now and forward
  Wavers the deep array ;
And on the tossing sea of steel,
  To and fro the standards reel ;
And the victorious trumpet-peal
  Dies fitfully away.

Yet one man for one moment
  Stood out before the crowd ;
Well known was he to all the Three,
  And they gave him greeting loud :
" Now welcome, welcome, Sextus !
  Now welcome to thy home !
Why dost thou stay, and turn away ?
  Here lies the road to Rome."

Thrice looked he at the city ;
  Thrice looked he at the dead ;
And thrice came on in fury,
  And thrice turned back in dread :
And, white with fear and hatred,
  Scowled at the narrow way
Where, wallowing in a pool of blood,
  The bravest Tuscans lay.

But meanwhile axe and lever
  Have manfully been plied ;
And now the bridge hangs tottering
  Above the boiling tide.
" Come back, come back, Horatius ! "
  Loud cried the Fathers all.
" Back, Lartius ! back, Herminius !
  Back, ere the ruin fall ! "

Back darted Spurius Lartius ;
　　Herminius darted back :
And, as they passed, beneath their feet
　　They felt the timbers crack.
But when they turned their faces,
　　And on the farther shore
Saw brave Horatius stand alone,
　　They would have crossed once more.

But with a crash like thunder
　　Fell every loosened beam,
And, like a dam, the mighty wreck
　　Lay right athwart the stream :
And a long shout of triumph
　　Rose from the walls of Rome,
As to the highest turret-tops
　　Was splashed the yellow foam.

And, like a horse unbroken
　　When first he feels the rein,
The furious river struggled hard,
　　And tossed his tawny mane,
And burst the curb, and bounded,
　　Rejoicing to be free,
And whirling down, in fierce career,
Battlement, and plank, and pier,
　　Rushed headlong to the sea.

Alone stood brave Horatius,
　　But constant still in mind ;
Thrice thirty thousand foes before,
　　And the broad flood behind.
" Down with him ! " cried false Sextus,
　　With a smile on his pale face.
" Now yield thee," cried Lars Porsena,
　　" Now yield thee to our grace."

Round turned he, as not deigning
    Those craven ranks to see ;
Nought spake he to Lars Porsena,
    To Sextus nought spake he ;
But he saw on Palatinus
    The white porch of his home ;
And he spake to the noble river
    That rolls by the towers of Rome.

" O Tiber ! father Tiber !
    To whom the Romans pray,
A Roman's life, a Roman's arms,
    Take thou in charge this day ! "
So he spake, and speaking sheathed
    The good sword by his side,
And with his harness on his back,
    Plunged headlong in the tide.

No sound of joy or sorrow
    Was heard from either bank ;
But friends and foes in dumb surprise,
With parted lips and straining eyes,
    Stood gazing where he sank ;
And when above the surges
    They saw his crest appear,
All Rome sent forth a rapturous cry,
And even the ranks of Tuscany
    Could scarce forbear to cheer.

But fiercely ran the current,
    Swollen high by months of rain :
And fast his blood was flowing ;
    And he was sore in pain,
And heavy with his armour,
    And spent with changing blows :
And oft they thought him sinking,
    But still again he rose.

Palatinus, One of the seven hills on which Rome was built.

Never, I ween, did swimmer,
   In such an evil case,
Struggle through such a raging flood
   Safe to the landing-place ;
But his limbs were borne up bravely
   By the brave heart within,
And our good father Tiber
   Bore bravely up his chin.

" Curse on him ! " quoth false Sextus ;
   " Will not the villain drown ?
But for this stay, ere close of day
   We should have sacked the town ! "
" Heaven help him ! " quoth Lars Porsena,
   " And bring him safe to shore ;
For such a gallant feat of arms
   Was never seen before."

And now he feels the bottom ;
   Now on dry earth he stands ;
Now round him throng the Fathers
   To press his gory hands ;
And now, with shouts and clapping,
   And noise of weeping loud,
He enters through the River-Gate,
   Borne by the joyous crowd.

They gave him of the corn-land,
   That was of public right,
As much as two strong oxen
   Could plough from morn till night ;
And they made a molten image,
   And set it up on high,
And there it stands unto this day
   To witness if I lie.

It stands in the Comitium
   Plain for all folk to see ;

Horatius in his harness,
  Halting upon one knee :
And underneath is written,
  In letters all of gold,
How valiantly he kept the bridge
  In the brave days of old.

And still his name sounds stirring
  Unto the men of Rome,
As the trumpet-blast that cries to them
  To charge the Volscian home ;
And wives still pray to Juno
  For boys with hearts as bold
As his who kept the bridge so well
  In the brave days of old.

And in the nights of winter,
  When the cold north winds blow,
And the long howling of the wolves
  Is heard amidst the snow ;
When round the lonely cottage
  Roars loud the tempest's din,
And the good logs of Algidus
  Roar louder yet within ;

When the oldest cask is opened,
  And the largest lamp is lit ;
When the chestnuts glow in the embers,
  And the kid turns on the spit ;
When young and old in circle
  Around the firebrands close ;
When the girls are weaving baskets,
  And the lads are shaping bows ;

When the goodman mends his armour,
  And trims his helmet's plume ;
When the goodwife's shuttle merrily
  Goes flashing through the loom ;

With weeping and with laughter
  Still is the story told,
How well Horatius kept the bridge
  In the brave days of old.

LORD MACAULAY.

What words would you use to describe this poem ?
Select what you consider to be the bravest lines ; the
most exciting ; the saddest ; the most inspiring ; the
best for expressing sense by sound.
What do you consider the crisis of the story ?
What is your opinion on (1) Sextus, (2) Lars Porsena ?
Use this stanza as a pattern for lines on the escape
of Prince Edward from his guards. (Read the story of
Simon de Montfort in your history book.)

To a Water-fowl

WHITHER, midst falling dew,
While glow the heavens with the last steps of day,
Far, through their rosy depths, dost thou pursue
  Thy solitary way ?

Vainly the fowler's eye
Might mark thy distant flight to do thee wrong,
As, darkly painted on the crimson sky,
  Thy figure floats along.

Seek'st thou the plashy brink
Of weedy lake, or marge of river wide,
Or where the rocking billows rise and sink
  On the chafed ocean side ?

There is a Power whose care
Teaches thy way along that pathless coast,
The desert and illimitable air,
  Lone wandering, but not lost.

All day thy wings have fanned,
At that far height, the cold thin atmosphere,

Yet stoop not, weary, to the welcome land,
    Though the dark night is near.

And soon that toil shall end ;
Soon shalt thou find a summer home, and rest,
And scream among thy fellows ; reeds shall bend,
    Soon, o'er thy sheltered nest.

Thou'rt gone, the abyss of heaven
Hath swallowed up thy form ; yet, on my heart,
Deeply hath sunk the lesson thou hast given,
    And shall not soon depart.

He who, from zone to zone,
Guides through the boundless sky thy certain flight,
In the long way that I must tread alone,
    Will lead my steps aright.

W. C. BRYANT.

Is this a story-poem or a poem of incident ?
At what time did the writer see the water-fowl ?
Try to make a drawing to illustrate the first verse.
What would the fowler try to do to the bird ?
If the bird were a wild duck would it be flying to lake, river, or sea ?

When the author (an American) wrote this poem he was in deep trouble. He was poor, and had scarcely a friend, and he did not know what to do for a living. One day he went out into the open country to think things over, and saw the water-fowl as he describes it in these verses. After this he felt more cheerful, and made up his mind to work very hard, feeling sure that things would all come right in the end. And they did. He got work ; he wrote many beautiful poems ; he married the lady he loved, and he lived, on the whole, a very happy and useful life.

Study the form of the verse—the length of the lines, the number of syllables in each line, the rhymes. Try to write a verse of this kind, say, about a robin :

    There is a bird whose breast
      Glows like a fire against the winter snow . . .

Can you go on ?

How do you think the poem should be read ?

What happened when " the abyss of heaven " swallowed up the form of the water-fowl ?

Could the author have told about the water-fowl in prose ?

Martin's Gift

Child. Is she for me ? Oh, thank you, Martin dear. What shall I call her ?

Martin, the Boatman. Well, sir, what you please.

Child. Then write on her *The Eagle.*

Martin.   Bless the child !
Eagle ! Why, you know nought of eagles, you.
When we lay off the coast, up Canada way,
And chanced to be ashore when twilight fell,
That was the place for eagles ; bald they were,
With eyes as yellow as gold.

Child.   Oh, Martin dear,
Tell me about them.

Martin. Tell ! there's nought to tell.
Only they snored at nights and frightened us.

Child. Snored ?

Martin. Ay, I tell you, snored ; they slept upright
In the great oaks by scores ; as true as time. . . .

                              When the moon was full,
I've seen them fish at night, in the middle watch,
When she got low. I've seen them plunge like stones,
And come up fighting with a fish as long,
Ay, longer than my arm, and they would sail
When they had struck its life out—they would sail—
Over the deck, and show their fell, fierce eyes,
And croon for pleasure, hug the prey, and speed
Grand as a frigate on a wind.

Child.   My ship,
She must be called *The Eagle*, after these.

                              JEAN INGELOW.

This is out of place in a poetry book, you say. It is a conversation or dialogue without any rhymes or regular

Which words from "Martin's Gift"
suit this picture?

stanzas. But the lines have a more or less regular beat,
which prose has not. Look at Martin's longest speech
and you will see what I mean. Further, the short lines
can be put together to make long ones. For example,

" What shall I call her ? " " Well, sir, what you
    please."

The piece is dramatic poetry, like a scene from a play.
There are good word-pictures in it. Which do you
think the clearest ?

How does the artist help out the story ?

Try to put a conversation from one of your school
reading-books into this dramatic form.

Prince Arthur and Hubert

A room in a castle.

Enter HUBERT *and* Executioners.

Hub. Heat me these irons hot ; and look thou stand
Within the arras : when I strike my foot
Upon the bosom of the ground, rush forth,
And bind the boy which you shall find with me
Fast to the chair : be heedful : hence, and watch.
    First Exec. I hope your warrant will bear out the
        deed.
    Hub. Uncleanly scruples ! fear not you : look to't.
                            [*Exeunt* Executioners.
Young lad, come forth ; I have to say with you.

Enter ARTHUR.

Arth. Good morrow, Hubert.
Hub.   Good morrow, little prince.
Arth. As little prince, having so great a title
To be more prince, as may be.   You are sad.
    Hub. Indeed, I have been merrier.
    Arth.   Mercy on me !
Methinks nobody should be sad but I :

Yet, I remember, when I was in France,
Young gentlemen would be as sad as night,
Only for wantonness.   By my christendom,
So I were out of prison and kept sheep,
I should be as merry as the day is long ;
And so I would be here, but that I doubt
My uncle practises more harm to me :
He is afraid of me and I of him :
Is it my fault that I was Geffrey's son ?
No, indeed, is't not ; and I would to heaven
I were your son, so you would love me, Hubert.

    Hub. (*aside*). If I talk to him, with his innocent
        prate
He will awake my mercy, which lies dead :
Therefore, I will be sudden and dispatch.

    Arth. Are you sick, Hubert ? you look pale to-day :
In sooth, I would you were a little sick,
That I might sit all night and watch with you :
I warrant I love you more than you do me.

    Hub. (*aside*). His words do take possession of my
        bosom.
Read here, young Arthur.   [*Showing a paper.*
               (*Aside*) How now, foolish rheum !
Turning dispiteous torture out of door !
I must be brief, lest resolution drop
Out at mine eyes in tender womanish tears.
Can you not read it ? is it not fair writ ?

    Arth. Too fairly, Hubert, for so foul effect :
Must you with hot irons burn out both mine eyes ?

    Hub. Young boy, I must.

    Arth.   And will you ?

    Hub.   And I will.

    Arth. Have you the heart ? When your head did
        but ache,
I knit my handkercher about your brows,
The best I had, a princess wrought it me,
And I did never ask it you again ;
And with my hand at midnight held your head,

And like the watchful minutes to the hour,
Still and anon cheered up the heavy time,
Saying, " What lack you ? " and " Where lies your
    grief ? "
Or " What good love may I perform for you ? "
Many a poor man's son would have lien still,
And ne'er have spoke a loving word to you ;
But you at your sick service had a prince.
Nay, you may think my love was crafty love,
And call it cunning : do, an if you will :
If heaven be pleased that you must use me ill,
Why then you must.   Will you put out mine eyes ?
These eyes that never did nor never shall
So much as frown on you.
    Hub.   I have sworn to do it ;
And with hot irons must I burn them out.
    Arth. Ah, none but in this iron age would do it !
The iron of itself, though heat red-hot,
Approaching near these eyes, would drink my tears
And quench his fiery indignation
Even in the matter of mine innocence ;
Nay, after that, consume away in rust,
But for containing fire to harm mine eye.
Are you more stubborn-hard than hammered iron ?
An if an angel should have come to me
And told me Hubert should put out mine eyes,
I would not have believed him,—no tongue but
    Hubert's.
    Hub. Come forth.   [*Stamps.*

Re-enter Executioners, *with a cord, irons, etc.*

Do as I bid you do.
    Arth. O, save me, Hubert, save me ! my eyes are out
Even with the fierce looks of these bloody men.
    Hub. Give me the iron, I say, and bind him here.
    Arth. Alas, what need you be so boisterous-rough ?
I will not struggle, I will stand stone-still.

For heaven sake, Hubert, let me not be bound !
Nay, hear me, Hubert, drive these men away,
And I will sit as quiet as a lamb ;
I will not stir, nor wince, nor speak a word,
Nor look upon the iron angerly :
Thrust but these men away, and I'll forgive you,
Whatever torment you do put me to.

    Hub. Go, stand within ; let me alone with him.

    First Exec. I am best pleased to be from such a deed.

                      [*Exeunt* Executioners.

    Arth. Alas, I then have chid away my friend !
He hath a stern look, but a gentle heart :
Let him come back, that his compassion may
Give life to yours.

    Hub.   Come, boy, prepare yourself.

    Arth. Is there no remedy ?

    Hub.   None, but to lose your eyes.

    Arth. O heaven, that there were but a mote in yours,
A grain, a dust, a gnat, a wandering hair,
Any annoyance in that precious sense !
Then, feeling what small things are boisterous there,
Your vile intent must needs seem horrible.

    Hub. Is this your promise ? go to, hold your tongue.

    Arth. Hubert, the utterance of a brace of tongues
Must needs want pleading for a pair of eyes :
Let me not hold my tongue, let me not, Hubert ;
Or, Hubert, if you will, cut out my tongue,
So I may keep mine eyes : oh, spare mine eyes,
Though to no use but still to look on you !
Lo, by my troth, the instrument is cold
And would not harm me.

    Hub.   I can heat it, boy.

    Arth. No, in good sooth ; the fire is dead with grief,
Being create for comfort, to be used
In undeserved extremes : see else yourself ;
There is no malice in this burning coal ;
The breath of heaven hath blown his spirit out
And strewed repentant ashes on his head.

Hub. But with my breath I can revive it, boy.

Arth. An if you do, you will but make it blush
And glow with shame of your proceedings, Hubert :
Nay, it perchance will sparkle in your eyes ;
And like a dog that is compelled to fight,
Snatch at his master that doth tarre him on.
All things that you should use to do me wrong
Deny their office : only you do lack
That mercy which fierce fire and iron extends,
Creatures of note for mercy-lacking uses.

Hub. Well, see to live ; I will not touch thine eyes
For all the treasure that thine uncle owes :
Yet am I sworn and I did purpose, boy,
With this same very iron to burn them out.

Arth. Oh, now you look like Hubert ! all this while
You were disguised.

Hub.   Peace ; no more. Adieu.
Your uncle must not know but you are dead ;
I'll fill these doggèd spies with false reports :
And, pretty child, sleep doubtless and secure,
That Hubert, for the wealth of all the world,
Will not offend thee.

Arth.   O heaven ! I thank you, Hubert.

Hub. Silence ; no more : go closely in with me :
Much danger do I undergo for thee.   [*Exeunt.*

WILLIAM SHAKESPEARE.
King John.

This is dramatic poetry from the play of *King John*,
by Shakespeare, the greatest poet of all poets.

The lines are, on the whole, of regular length, though now
and again they trip up or stumble, just to make a change.

The short lines go together to make long ones.

The regular line has five feet of two syllables each,
with the stress on the second syllable.

Young lad | come forth ; | I have | to say | with you.

Which do you consider the most pitiful part ; the most
exciting ; the most pleasing ?

This is a fine scene for acting.

Sam's Three Wishes; or, Life's Little Whirligig

" I'm thinking and thinking," said old Sam Shore,
" 'Twere somebody *knocking* I heard at the door."

From the clock popped the cuckoo and cuckooed out
    eight,
As there in his chair he wondering sate. . . .
" There's no one I knows on would come so late,
A-clicking the latch of an empty house
With nobbut inside 'un but me and a mouse. . . .
Maybe a-waking in sleep I be,
And 'twere out of a dream came that tapping to me."
At length he cautiously rose, and went,
And with thumb upon latch awhile listening bent,
Then slowly drew open the door. And behold !
There stood a Fairy !—all green and gold,
Mantled up warm against dark and cold,
And smiling up into his candle-shine,
Lips like wax, and cheeks like wine,
As saucy and winsome a thing to see
As are linden buds on a linden tree.
Stock-still in the doorway stood simple Sam,
A-ducking his head, with " Good-e'en to 'ee, Ma'am."

Dame Fairy she nods, and cries clear and sweet,
" 'Tis a *very* good-e'en, sir, when such folks meet.
I know thee, Sam, though thou wist not of me,
And I'm come in late gloaming to speak with thee ;
Though my eyes do dazzle at glint of your rush,
All under this pretty green fuchsia bush."

Sam ducked once more, smiling simple and slow.
Like the warbling of birds her words did flow,

And she laughed, very merry, to see how true
Shone the old man's kindness his courtesy through.
And she nodded her head, and the stars on high
Sparkled down on her smallness from out of the sky.
" A friend is a friend, Sam, and wonderful pleasant,
And I'm come for old sake's sake to bring thee a
        present.
Three wishes, three wishes are thine, Sam Shore,
Just three wishes—and wish no more,
All because, ruby-ripe to see,
The pixy-pears burn in yon hawthorn tree,
And your old milch cow, wheresoever she goes
Never crops over the fairy-knowes.
Ay, Sam, thou art old and thy house is lone,
But there's Potencies round thee, and here is one ! "

Poor Sam, he stared : and the stars o'erhead
A shimmering light on the elm-tops shed.
Like rilling of water her voice rang sweet,
And the night-wind sighed at the sound of it.
He frowned—glanced back at the empty grate,
And shook very slowly his grey old pate :
" Three wishes, my dear !   Why, I scarcely knows
Which be my crany and which my toes !
But I thank 'ee, Ma'am, kindly, and this I'd say,
That the night of your passing is Michaelmas Day ;
And if it were company come on a sudden,
Why, I'd ax for a fat goose to fry in the oven ! "

And lo, and forsooth ! as the words he was uttering,
A rich puff of air set his candle a-guttering,
And there rose in the kitchen a sizzling and sputtering,
With a crackling of sparks and of flames a great
        fluttering,
And—of which there could not be two opinions—
A smoking-hot savour of sage and—onions.
Beam, wall, and flagstones the kitchen was lit,
Every dark corner and cranny of it,

With the blaze from the hearthstone. Copper and brass
Winked back the winking of platter and glass.
And a wonderful squeaking of mice went up
At the smell of a Michaelmas supper to sup—
Unctuous odours that wreathed and swirled
Where'er frisked a whisker or mouse-tail twirled,
While out of the chimney up into the night
That ne'er-to-be-snuffed-too-much smoke took flight.
" That's one," says the Fairy, finger on thumb,
" So now, Mister Sam, there's but two to come ! "

She leaned her head sidelong ; she lifted her chin,
With a twinkling of eye from the radiance within.
Poor Sam stood 'stounded ; he says, says he,
" I *wish* my old Mother was back with me,
For if there was one thing she couldn't refuse
'Twas a sweet thick slice from the breast of a goose."
But his cheek grew stiff and his eyes stared bright,
For there, on her stick, pushing out of the night,
Tap-tapping along, herself and no other,
Came who but the shape of his dear old Mother !
Straight into the kitchen she hastened and went,
Her breath coming quick as if all but spent,
" Why, Sam," says she, " the bird be turning,
For my nose tells I that the skin's a-burning ! "
And down at the oven the ghost of her sat
And basted the goose with the boiling fat.

" Oho," cries the Fairy, sweet and small,
" Another wish gone will leave nothing at all."
And Sam sighs, " Bless 'ee, Ma'am, keep the other,
There's nowt that I want now I have my Mother."
But the Fairy laughs softly, and says, says she,
" There's one wish left, Sam, I promised 'ee three.
Hasten your wits, the hour creeps on,
There's calling afield and I'm soon to be gone.
Soon as haps midnight the cocks will crow
And me to the gathering and feasting must go."

Sam gazed at his Mother—withered and wan,
The rose in her cheek, her bright hair, gone,
And her poor old back bent double with years—
And he scarce could speak for the salt, salt tears.
" Well, well," he says, " I'm unspeakable glad :
But—it bain't quite the same as when I was a lad.
There's joy and there's joy, Ma'am, but to tell 'ee the
     truth,
There's none can compare with the joy of one's youth.
And if it was possible, how could I choose
But be back in boy's breeches to eat the goose ;
And all the old things—and my Mother the most,
To shine again real as my own gatepost.
What wouldn't I give, too, to see again wag
The dumpity tail of my old dog, Shag !
Your kindness, Ma'am, but all wishing was vain
Unless us can both be young again."
A shrill, faint laughter from nowhere came . . .
Empty the dark in the candle-flame. . . .

And there stood our Sam, about four foot high,
Snub nose, shock hair, and round blue eye.
Breeches and braces and coat of him too,
Shirt on his back, and each clodhopping shoe
Had shrunk to a nicety—button and hem—
To fit the small Sammie tucked up into them.

There was his Mother, too ; smooth, clear cheek,
Lips as sooth as a blackbird's beak,
Pretty arched eyebrows, the daintiest nose—
While the smoke of the baking deliciously rose.
" Come, Sammie," she cries, " your old Mammikin's
     joy,
Climb up on your stool, supper's ready, my boy,
Bring in the candle, and shut out the night ;
There's goose, baked taties and cabbage to bite.
Why, bless the wee lamb, he's all shiver and shake,
And you'd think from the look of him scarcely awake !

If 'ee glour wi' those eyes, Sam, so dark and round,
The elves will away with 'ee, I'll be bound!"
So Sam and his Mother by wishes three
Were made just as happy as happy can be.
And there—with a bumpity tail to wag—
Sat laughing, with tongue out, their old dog, Shag.
To clatter of platter, bones, giblets and juice,
Between them they ate up the whole of the goose.

But time is a river for ever in flow,
The weeks went by as the weeks must go.
Soon fifty-two to a year did grow.
The long years passed, one after another,
Making older and older our Sam and his Mother;
And, alas and alack, with nine of them gone,
Poor Shag lay asleep again under a stone.
And a sorrowful dread would sometimes creep
Into Sam's dreams, as he lay asleep,
That his Mother was lost, and away he'd fare,
Calling her, calling her, everywhere,
In dark, in rain, by roads unknown,
Under echoing hills, and alone, alone.
What bliss in the morning to wake and see
The sun shining green in the linden tree,
And out of that dream's dark shadowiness
To slip in on his Mother and give her a kiss.
Then go whistling off in the dew to hear
The thrushes all mocking him, sweet and clear.

Still, moon after moon from heaven above
Shone on Mother and son, and made light of love.
Her roses faded, her pretty brown hair
Had sorrowful grey in it everywhere,
And at last she died, and was laid to rest,
Her tired hands crossed on her shrunken breast.
And Sam, now lonely, lived on and on
Till most of his workaday life seemed gone.

Yet spring came again with its green and blue,
And presently summer's wild roses too,
Pinks, sweet-william, and sops-in-wine,
Blackberry, lavender, eglantine.
And when these had blossomed and gone their way,
'Twas apples, and daisies and Michaelmas Day—
Yes, spider-webs, dew, and haws in the may,
And seraphs singing in Michaelmas Day.

Sam worked all morning and *couldn't* get rest
For a kind of a feeling of grief in his breast.
And yet, not grief, but something more
Like the thought that what happens has happened
    before.
He fed the chickens, he fed the sow,
On a three-legged stool sate down to the cow,
With a pail 'twixt his legs in the green in the meadow,
Under the elm trees' lengthening shadow ;
And woke at last with a smile and a sigh
To find he had milked his poor Jingo dry.

As dusk set in, even the birds did seem
To be calling and calling from out of a dream.
He chopped up kindling, shut up his shed,
In a bucket of well-water soused his head
To freshen his eyes up a little and make
The drowsy old wits of him wider awake.
As neat as a womanless creature is able,
He swept up his hearthstone and laid the table.
And then o'er his platter and mug, if you please,
Sate gloomily gooming at loaf and cheese—
Gooming and gooming as if the mere sight
Of his victuals could satisfy appetite !
And the longer and longer he looked at them
The slimmer slimmed upward his candle flame,
Blue in the air. And when squeaked a mouse
'Twas loud as a trump in the hush of the house,

Then, sudden, a soft little wind puffed by,
'Twixt the thick-thatched roof and the star-sown sky ;
And died.   And then
That deep, dead, wonderful silence again.

Then—soft as a rattle a-counting her seeds
In the midst of a tangle of withered-up weeds—
Came a faint, faint knocking, a rustle like silk,
And a breath at the keyhole as soft as milk—
Still as the flit of a moth.   And then . . .
That infinitesimal knocking again.

Sam lifted his chin from his fists.   He listened.
His wandering eyes in the candle glistened.
Then slowly, slowly, rolled round by degrees—
And there sat a mouse on the top of his cheese.
He stared at this Midget, and it at him,
Over the edge of his mug's round rim,
And—as if it were Christian—he says, " Did 'ee hear
A faint little tap-tap-tap-tapping, my dear ?
You was at supper and me in a maze,
'Tis dark for a caller in these lone days,
There's nowt in the larder.   We're both of us old.
And all of my loved ones sleep under the mould,
And yet—and yet—as I've told 'ee before . . ."

But if Sam's story you'd read to the end,
Turn back to page one, and press onward, dear friend ·
Yes, if you would stave the last note of this song,
Turn back to page primus, and warble along !
For all sober records of life (come to write 'em),
Are bound to continue—well—ad infinitum !

WALTER DE LA MARE.

One's thoughts about this poem may run in several
directions. For myself, I like to dwell on the pictures
of the cottage interior, and to try to recall the lovely
and mysterious sounds and—a more difficult matter—to

inhale the satisfying odours and feel the glow of the warm fire.

Were you expecting Sam to ask for something else ? Do you think he would have been happy if the fairy had made him squire or had sent him to live in London ? Remember that he had his three great chances.

Fortunately Sam's simple, useful, loving life, with its love of home and mother, its delight in simple things, does go on for ever in this land of ours, though he may not always be called Sam.

The Highwayman

PART ONE

THE wind was a torrent of darkness among the gusty
    trees,
The moon was a ghostly galleon tossed upon cloudy
    seas,
The road was a ribbon of moonlight over the purple
    moor,
And the highwayman came riding—
        Riding—riding—
The highwayman came riding, up to the old inn-door.

He'd a French cocked hat on his forehead, a bunch of
    lace at his chin,
A coat of claret velvet, and breeches of brown doe-
    skin ;
They fitted with never a wrinkle : his boots were up
    to the thigh !
And he rode with a jewelled twinkle,
        His pistol butts a-twinkle,
His rapier hilt a-twinkle, under the jewelled sky.

Over the cobbles he clattered and clashed in the
    dark inn-yard,
And he tapped with his whip on the shutters, but all
    was locked and barred ;

He whistled a tune to the window, and who should be
     waiting there
But the landlord's black-eyed daughter,
        Bess, the landlord's daughter,
Plaiting a dark red love-knot into her long black hair.

And dark in the dark old inn-yard a stable wicket
     creaked,
Where Tim the ostler listened ; his face was white and
     peaked ;
His eyes were hollows of madness, his hair like mouldy
     hay,
But he loved the landlord's daughter,
        The landlord's red-lipped daughter ;
Dumb as a dog he listened, and he heard the robber
     say—

" One kiss, my bonny sweetheart, I'm after a prize
     to-night,
But I shall be back with the yellow gold before the
     morning light ;
Yet, if they press me sharply, and harry me through
     the day,
Then look for me by moonlight,
        Watch for me by moonlight,
I'll come to thee by moonlight, though hell should
     bar the way."

He rose upright in the stirrups ; he scarce could reach
     her hand,
But she loosened her hair i' the casement ! His face
     burnt like a brand
As the black cascade of perfume came tumbling over
     his breast ;
And he kissed its waves in the moonlight,
        (Oh, sweet black waves in the moonlight !)
Then he tugged at his rein in the moonlight, and
     galloped away to the West.

PART TWO

He did not come in the dawning ; he did not come at
noon ;
And out o' the tawny sunset, before the rise o' the
moon,
When the road was a gipsy's ribbon, looping the
purple moor,
A red-coat troop came marching—
Marching—marching—
King George's men came marching, up to the old
inn-door.

They said no word to the landlord, they drank his ale
instead,
But they gagged his daughter and bound her to the
foot of her narrow bed ;
Two of them knelt at the casement, with muskets at
their side !
There was death at every window,
And hell at one dark window ;
For Bess could see, through her casement, the road
that he would ride.

They had tied her up to attention, with many a
sniggering jest ;
They had bound a musket beside her, with the barrel
beneath her breast !
" Now keep good watch ! " and they kissed her.
She heard the dead man say—
Look for me by moonlight ;
Watch for me by moonlight ;
I'll come to thee by moonlight, though hell should bar the
way !

She twisted her hands behind her ; but all the knots
held good !

She writhed her hands till her fingers were wet with
    sweat or blood !
They stretched and strained in the darkness, and the
    hours crawled by like years,
Till, now, on the stroke of midnight,
       Cold, on the stroke of midnight,
The tip of one finger touched it !   The trigger at last
    was hers !

The tip of one finger touched it ; she strove no more
    for the rest !
Up she stood up to attention, with the barrel beneath
    her breast,
She would not risk their hearing ; she would not
    strive again ;
For the road lay bare in the moonlight,
       Blank and bare in the moonlight ;
And the blood of her veins in the moonlight throbbed
    to her love's refrain.

Tlot-tlot ; tlot-tlot !   Had they heard it ?   The horse-
    hoofs ringing clear ;
Tlot-tlot, tlot-tlot, in the distance !   Were they deaf
    that they did not hear ?
Down the ribbon of moonlight, over the brow of the
    hill,
The highwayman came riding,
       Riding, riding !
The red-coats looked to their priming !   She stood
    up, straight and still.

Tlot-tlot, in the frosty silence !   *Tlot-tlot,* in the echo-
    ing night !
Nearer he came and nearer !   Her face was like a
    light !
Her eyes grew wide for a moment ; she drew one last
    deep breath,

Then her finger moved in the moonlight,
>Her musket shattered the moonlight,
Shattered her breast in the moonlight and warned
him—with her death.

He turned ; he spurred to the westward ; he did not
know who stood
Bowed, with her head o'er musket, drenched with her
own red blood !
Not till the dawn he heard it, and slowly blanched to
hear
How Bess, the landlord's daughter,
>The landlord's black-eyed daughter,
Had watched for her love in the moonlight, and died
in the darkness there.

Back, he spurred like a madman, shrieking a curse to
the sky,
With the white road smoking behind him, and his
rapier brandished high !
Blood-red were his spurs i' the golden noon ; wine-
red was his velvet coat ;
When they shot him down on the highway,
>Down like a dog on the highway,
And he lay in his blood on the highway, with the
bunch of lace at his throat.

*And still of a winter's night, they say, when the wind
is in the trees,*
*When the moon is a ghostly galleon tossed upon cloudy
seas,*
*When the road is a ribbon of moonlight over the purple
moor,*
A highwayman comes riding—
>*Riding—riding—*
A highwayman comes riding, up to the old inn-door.

*Over the cobbles he clatters and clangs in the dark inn-
        yard;*
*And he taps with his whip on the shutters, but all is
        locked and barred;*
*He whistles a tune to the window, and who should be
        waiting there*
But the landlord's black-eyed daughter,
        Bess, the landlord's daughter,
Plaiting a dark red love-knot into her long black hair.

ALFRED NOYES.

What does the poet make you see in the first three
lines (perhaps you can sketch it?), and what does he
make you hear in the next three lines? What do you find
your eyelids doing near the end of the second stanza?

What words are repeated again and again, and why?
Which is the most exciting line in the story?
Make a list of the actors in the story. Would it make
a good film?
If a good artist offered to make you a picture to go
with this poem, what would you ask him to show in it?
What do you think Tim the ostler said about it all?

A Ballad-Maker

ONCE I loved a maiden fair,
    Over the hills and far away,
Lands she had and lovers to spare,
    Over the hills and far away.
And I was stooped and troubled sore,
And my face was pale, and the coat I wore
Was thin as my supper the night before.
    Over the hills and far away.

Once I passed in the autumn late,
    Over the hills and far away,

Her bawn and byre and painted gate,
   Over the hills and far away.
She was leaning there in the twilight space,
Sweet sorrow was on her fair young face,
And her wistful eyes were away from the place—
   Over the hills and far away.

Maybe she thought as she watched me come,
   Over the hills and far away,
With my awkward stride, and my face so glum,
   Over the hills and far away,
" Spite of his stoop, he still is young ;
They say he goes the Shee among,
Ballads he makes, I've heard them sung
   Over the hills and far away."

She gave me good-night in gentle wise,
   Over the hills and far away,
Shyly lifting to mine, dark eyes,
   Over the hills and far away.
What could I do but stop and speak,
And she no longer proud but meek ?
She plucked me a rose like her wild-rose cheek—
   Over the hills and far away.

To-morrow, Mavourneen a sleeveen weds,
   Over the hills and far away,
With corn in haggard and cattle in sheds,
   Over the hills and far away.
And I who have lost her—the dear, the rare—
Well, I got me this ballad to sing at the fair,
'Twill bring enough money to drown my care,
   Over the hills and far away.

                               PADRAIC COLUM.

There are some Irish words in this poem the meaning
of which can be easily guessed.

What had this ballad-maker learnt about his trade from the old ballads ? What had he not been able to learn or did not care to imitate ?

What do I mean if I say that this poem is " pictorial " ?

Does the poet tell us the girl's name ?

Which of the ballads in this book might this ballad-maker have written ?

THE END

WITHDRAWN

PRINTED IN GREAT BRITAIN AT
THE PRESS OF THE PUBLISHERS

PATTERN POETRY
PART I

¶ This volume is intended for Junior Forms, and contains a collection of verses in great variety, beginning with the prentice efforts of young children, and passing through folk-songs, dance poems, simple ballads, and story poems to longer narrative pieces like *John Gilpin*, *The Pied Piper*, *The Romaunt of the Page*, and *Goblin Market*.

¶ In addition to the traditional pieces and poems by standard authors, a large number of poems of to-day are included—by Laurence Binyon, Walter de la Mare, Katharine Tynan, J. J. Bell, Alfred Noyes, Moira O'Neill, John Masefield, Harold Monro, etc.

PATTERN POETRY
PART II

¶ This is an anthology for Middle Form pupils, arranged on a new and interesting plan which is designed to interest the pupil in the form as well as the content of English poetry.

¶ The pieces are standard and modern in great variety, and many exercises are suggested which will help towards the truest appreciation and enjoyment.

THOMAS NELSON AND SONS, LTD
LONDON, EDINBURGH, AND NEW YORK

By the same Editor

PATTERN POETRY
PART III

A Book of Longer Poems, from Chaucer to
Francis Thompson

¶ The poems of this book are arranged in chronological order, and include—CHAUCER : *Prologue* ; SPENSER : *St. George and the Dragon* ; MILTON : *Christ's Nativity* and *Lycidas* ; DRYDEN : *Alexander's Feast* ; POPE : *Rape of the Lock* ; GRAY : *Elegy* ; GOLDSMITH : *Deserted Village* ; BURNS : *Cotter's Saturday Night* ; WORDSWORTH : *Tintern Abbey* and *Intimations of Immortality* ; COLERIDGE : *Ancient Mariner* ; SHELLEY : *Adonais* ; KEATS : *Ode to a Nightingale* and *Ode on a Grecian Urn* ; TENNYSON : *Lotos Eaters, Dream of Fair Women,* and *Morte d'Arthur* ; BROWNING : *Abt Vogler* and *Andrea del Sarto* ; ARNOLD : *The Scholar Gipsy* ; ROSSETTI : *The Blessèd Damozel* ; SWINBURNE : *A Swimmer's Dream* ; FRANCIS THOMPSON : *The Hound of Heaven*. The collection is therefore not only varied, but more or less representative of English poetry.

¶ Each poem is followed by a Commentary dealing with matters of form, style, diction, and theme, with notes on the author designed to help in the understanding and appreciation of the particular poem under review.

THOMAS NELSON AND SONS, LTD.

LONDON, EDINBURGH, AND NEW YORK